SCEPTRE

The Agony
& the Ecstasy

New Writing for the World Cup

Edited by NICHOLAS ROYLE

SCEPTRE

First published in 1998 by Hodder and Stoughton
A division of Hodder Headline PLC
A Sceptre Paperback

A CIP catalogue record for this book is
available from the British Library

ISBN 0 340 71241 4

Typeset by Palimpsest Book Production Limited,
Polmont, Stirlingshire
Printed and bound in Great Britain by
Clays Ltd, St Ives PLC, Bungay, Suffolk

Hodder and Stoughton
A division of Hodder Headline PLC
338 Euston Road
London NW1 3BH

For David & Ruth

Contents

Squelch!

Introduction by Nicholas Royle

Watching the 1970 World Cup is one of my earliest memories. What I remember – from black and white television, from colour spreads in the *Observer Magazine* – are the tidy rows of tanned faces and white shirts, tier upon tier of Mexicans behind the goals, in the stands, like witnesses at some kind of unguessable, ancient ceremony. While on the pitch, tired men in white walked with the ball, played the simplest of passes. Frazzled by the heat, sick of the altitude. Bobby Moore, dignified in defeat. Colin Bell and Francis Lee, unlucky ambassadors from Maine Road, my home turf.

Mexico '70 was judged worthy of having a slightly racy car named after it (a limited-edition mark one Ford Escort). Even the West Germans were exciting. With the war only 25 years in the past and my toy cupboard bursting with Airfix armies, I inevitably perceived them as the enemy, and perhaps for this reason their names fired my imagination. Karlheinz Schnellinger, Franz Beckenbauer, Gerd Müller, Uwe Seeler, Sepp Maier. I scanned their faces for traces of a dark history and found none. And yet, was not a certain tarnished glamour conferred upon them by my reading of *Commando* comics and by the whole baffling business of the Cold War? If these were the West Germans, who and where were the East Germans? I had postage stamps from the DDR, which proved the place existed, so why didn't they play in the

World Cup – were they not allowed to? (They reached the finals four years later, going out in the second round despite having won their group, beating their western counterparts into second place; West Germany, of course, went on to win the tournament.)

Also remembering 1970 as if it were yesterday – and just about old enough to do so – are exiled writers David Flusfeder and Peterjon Cresswell. Their memoirs pick out a couple of individual stories, in addition to their own: Flusfeder wonders what Gordon Banks must have been feeling, laid low with a stomach complaint, and Cresswell studies Brazil's fourth goal against Italy, Carlos Alberto's contribution to the gallery of great sporting moments. Screenwriter Colin Shindler, meanwhile, transposes his pin-sharp recollections of the 1970 campaign to a fictional setting.

When I started work on this anthology, I had to be careful not to fill its pages with memories of Mexico, to the exclusion of all other campaigns, so precise, so powerful, so poignant are my own memories of that time. I first encountered the phrase 'The Agony & The Ecstasy' in a newspaper headline about one of England's key games in 1970, no doubt accompanied by contrasting, grainy black and white photographs of, say, Bobby Moore and Gerd Müller, or Francis Lee and Pelé. It would have been in one of four papers – the *Guardian*, the *Manchester Evening News*, the *Observer* or possibly the *Sunday Times*. We can probably rule out the *Sale & Altrincham Messenger* (where I began my career in journalism, as a paper boy). In fact, we can definitely rule it out – along with the *MEN* – because the Royle family had not yet moved back to Manchester from Newcastle-upon-Tyne.

Twenty years later – another World Cup, the streets of Britain deserted, this time a semi-final defeat at the hands of Beckenbauer & Co. I was going to be watching the game with my old friend Nigel at his flat in Brixton. His Japanese wife Yuka came with us to Manchester City's London-based fixtures, which in those days meant trips to Stamford Bridge, Highbury and White Hart Lane, as it hopefully will do again before too long. Yuka had yet to be gripped by her mysterious and short-lived compulsion to support

Nottingham Forest; she has since returned to the fold and remains loyal despite the pair having relocated to Tokyo for the foreseeable future.

On that night, that semi-final night, I was accompanied by a new girlfriend. Nigel had not yet met her and I was anxious to obtain his approval. We were in a difficult and complex Situation, she and I, and something had to give. It could have gone either way, and it's tempting to believe, in such moments, especially if you're a bit soft in the head and your judgement's affected, that the outcome of a Situation depends entirely on the result of a football game. Your destiny in the hands of Paul Gascoigne.

I couldn't help feeling that if England beat Germany, we'd end up staying together. And, conversely, that if the Deutschers did the dirty on our brave boys, it would be curtains for the two of us.

Brixton was a ghost town as we ran from the Tube to Nigel's flat. Nigel believed I was always late for things. You could see his point: I was always late for things. But it was my ongoing resolution to be on time.

Especially for this.

We were on time. England were on form. But it didn't work out.

I can't remember what Nigel thought of my companion, but it didn't work out with her either. It didn't work out quite spectacularly.

Novelist, short story writer, biographer and critic DJ Taylor recalls that same night's sense of disappointment in his short story, while two writers who have published acclaimed books on football – Pete Davies and Pete May – offer radically different accounts of their own experiences of Italia '90.

In 1990, my views on the West Germans had become no more reasonable than they had been in 1970, but they had at least changed. I mean, were they lucky, or were they cheats? They always seemed to win, despite scarcely deserving to. This distorted perception of the Germans has persisted in me up to the present day and while I realise I should grow out of it, I seem unable – or unwilling – to do so. I fully expect Germany to carry off the trophy again in France '98, and to achieve it by a series of dubious refereeing decisions, Olympic dives, Golden Goals and time-wasting.

Even now when I look back at footage of the quarter-final in 1970, I see, in the second period of extra time, several West German players falling to the ground in apparent agony – thunder-thighed Uwe Seeler, the mighty Beckenbauer himself, black-clad 'keeper Sepp Maier – three stooges giving every indication of being as guilty of overacting as would Jürgen Klinsmann twenty years later.

Frankly I couldn't bear it if they were to win again. My heart says England will win the trophy (despite their disappointing result against Chile at Wembley back in February), while my head opts for the Germans – the Manchester bloody United of World Cup football.

If my position vis-à-vis the German team appears to overstep the line between passion and chauvinism, let us be thankful for Dave Rimmer who corrects the balance in his memoir. Having lived in Berlin for eight years, he seems uniquely well-placed to do this.

But what of the Brazilians, deserving winners in 1970 and possibly the real reason why that campaign, Franny Lee and Colin Bell notwithstanding, made an indelible impression on me? The names again – Rivelino, Jairzinho, Tostao, the breathtaking Pelé. Even a seven-year-old boy could see there was something magical about them. No doubt their descendants will entertain us in France. More exciting than the moon landings, Mexico '70 was commemorated by Esso garages where you could pick up silver coins bearing the likenesses of the England players, and little booklets, three inches by two, known as *Squelchers!*. Taking another look at my *Squelchers!* twenty-eight years later – I have a full set of sixteen in a blue plastic wallet which I will treasure until the day my final whistle blows – I see they were edited by one Leslie Vernon. A fine piece of work, Leslie Vernon, if by chance you are reading this. Among the incorrect assertions to get squelched was the following: 'Pigeons were released before every match in the 1970 World Cup to create a breeze and relieve the intense heat'. 'SQUELCH! No. It was a superb piece of showmanship to delight the Mexican crowds.' And: 'England are the only side ever to have won the World Cup at home.' 'SQUELCH! Three countries have won the World Cup at home: Uruguay in 1930, Italy in 1934, and England in 1966.' Since then, of course, it has been won at home by West Germany (1974) and Argentina (1978).

Novelist Conrad Williams was seduced, in Warrington at the age of nine, by eleven men with dark, streaming hair and exotic-sounding names – the Argentina side which triumphed at home. Jimmy Burns, Maradona's intrepid biographer, turns his attention to Argentina's shame of 1978 in his first published short story, while novelist Ben Richards casts a critical but affectionate eye over Argentina's neighbours Chile in his non-fiction contribution. England's 1966 success inspires very different short stories by novelists Graham Joyce and Mark Morris. Returning to Maradona, the Argentine genius is the subject of a piece by comedian and novelist David Baddiel, part of which first appeared in a different form in the *Daily Telegraph*.

Each a widely published journalist and author, Steve Grant and Maureen Freely both perceive the regularity of the World Cup as having a certain significance in their lives: Grant measures his son's life by the four-yearly jamboree (junior was born the day that Holland beat Italy and Brazil beat Peru in 1978), and Freely, you can be sure, will always be wandering up and down Church Row in Hampstead, north London, come the opening ceremony. Another contributor whose memoir is based more on match avoidance than attendance is novelist Rupert Thomson – as you will see, he did have a few better offers than USA '94 was able to extend.

*　　*　　*

The thing is, with anthologies, as editor one has to decide whether or not to include a contribution by oneself. Any writer with a box-file full of rejection slips, suddenly finding himself in the position of only having himself to please, is tempted to slot one home. The view I take as a *reader* is generally a dim one, since it's surely the editor's job to present the work of other writers, whereas to showcase one's own efforts and imply that they match the quality of other contributions strays dangerously close to an act of vanity. But then many editors do it and get away with it, either because they make a joke about it (in the acknowledgements for his anthology *The Far Reaches of Fear*, editor Ramsey Campbell included the following: 'Ramsey Campbell for *The Pattern*. Copyright 1976 by Ramsey Campbell. Thank you, he said, shaking himself by the hand') or by evincing a modicum of self-deprecation and then writing a piece as charming and entertaining as Simon Kuper's own contribution to *Perfect Pitch 1: Home Ground*.

The thing you mustn't do, of course, is go on and on about your dilemma in the introduction.

For a previous anthology of football short stories which bore my name, the conceit was that instead of being the editor I was in fact the referee. So I did a bit of research to see if a referee had ever scored a goal in professional football which had been allowed to stand. If there were such a precedent then I felt I would be able to get away with including a story of my own. A nice man called Ivan Robinson confirmed for me that such a thing had indeed happened, long ago, in a third-division match between Doncaster and Torquay, or Plymouth and Barrow, I don't know, someone like that. The ball struck the referee and went in the net and he allowed it to stand. Therefore, I had exactly what I wanted, I could put myself in the book. But in the end I chose not to. I mean, imagine if my piece were dismayingly awful compared to all the others, or even just not *quite* as good, the embarrassment factor would be through the roof.

(The anthology to which I refer is the now almost legendary *A*

Book of Two Halves, a copy of which I saw the other day on the Contemporary Classics table in Waterstone's.

 I put it there.)

So for *this* book, my nominal role is coach rather than referee. It should be easy to justify picking myself for the team – a player-manager giving himself a run-out. Yet still, I couldn't quite do it. But then I thought why not? All you need to do is call it the introduction and no one's bothered.

I enjoyed USA '94, though of course I was disappointed that England were not involved. I watched most games on my own, with no interruptions, in my flat in South Tottenham, north London.

I was single, finally over all the deadly fall-out from the Situation which dated back to Italia '90, and just beginning to think about sticking my head out the door of life again, as it were. Within a matter of weeks I would meet a lovely woman called Kate, who is now my wife, and together we have a little boy, Charlie. We met on Saturday 20 August 1994 outside the Market Bar in Notting Hill. I was fresh from watching City lose 3-0 at Highbury – it was the opening day of the football season. And just in case anyone thinks I'm coming on all Nick Hornby, going on about my personal life and how it ties in with football, I should perhaps point out that I've never read him, even if I am the only person on the planet who hasn't.

So will France triumph this time around, being the host nation? Or will it be Brazil, Germany or England? Or, for that matter, Scotland, on whose habit of snatching 'defeat from the jaws of victory' Scots novelist, poet and short story writer Ron Butlin ruminates in his contribution. Another habitué of the short form – habitué in that he's published one previous short story, also about football – Tim Lawler considers the ramifications of Jamaica's first trip to the World Cup finals.

Politics and comedy come together to produce very different

results in the short stories of Rosie Jackson and Tom Bromley; both pieces are set around the 1998 competition. As is Christopher Kenworthy's short story, although the heartstopping events he describes are decidedly tragic rather than comic.

Any one of thirty-two teams could win the World Cup this July, and whatever the result, it will render my speculations on the possible outcome redundant. But not so the twenty-four pieces of original writing which follow. United – how I hate that word since it's been hijacked by Old Trafford suits, much to the disgust, I'm sure, of football fans in Leeds, Newcastle, Sheffield and elsewhere – united by their quality and a shared theme of World Cup football, these contributions include, as I have attempted to describe, both fiction and non-fiction, and a few pieces where the two merge to create a kind of creative memoir. The contributors between them cover World Cup campaigns from 1934 (the inimitable Nick Rogers gets familiar with the *Azzurri*) to 2010 (Geoff Nicholson takes drugs in sport to the inevitable conclusion) via some timeless post-apocalyptic moment (Chaz Brenchley must have been using some of Geoff Nicholson's drugs to have come up with *his* bizarre short story). But as with all good writing, the stories here, fiction and non-fiction, are timeless and of lasting value and will therefore give just as much pleasure and enlightenment if reread, or indeed if read for the first time, *after* the 1998 World Cup finals, which I for one am looking forward to with mounting excitement as 10 June draws nearer. I'll be doing my best to watch every game, work commitments and baby son allowing. (Little Charlie will be one year old on the day South Africa play Denmark, and France take on Saudi Arabia.)

A brief note on the way the contents have been organised: the book has been divided into two halves, almost – goodness me – like a game of football. The Agony first, and then The Ecstasy. This does not mean that the first twelve pieces are all doom and gloom while the second lot are all airy-fairy, pie in the sky. You might well feel there's more ecstasy in The Agony than agony, and more agony in The Ecstasy than ecstasy, but don't worry about it. It's not to be taken too seriously.

Finally, I'd just like to thank a few people. I'm grateful to all the authors for their participation; to my editor at Sceptre, Neil Taylor, whose idea the book was; and to Andrew Shields who answered a lot of dull research queries with admirable patience. I'd also like to acknowledge the support of my wife, who absorbed rising stress levels with no outward effect. Most of all, thanks to you, the reader, for shelling out seven quid. (Surely you can't have read *this* far while standing in the bookshop?) Now it's all yours.

Nicholas Royle
London, March 1998

THE AGONY

Sportsview

David Flusfeder

I was six when I came to this country. I was glad to come here. England was smaller and greyer than America which made me consequently larger and more colourful. In New Jersey I had been the youngest in my class. In London I was among the oldest. I won playground races. I could read better than anyone else, except for one plump girl called Nicola who welcomed me and resented me and tried to make me her boyfriend and who will take no further part in this story.

The hardest test was put to me by every boy I had a conversation with. It was asked by my runny-nosed deskmate and it was asked in every corner of class room, dining hall, playground,

– What football team do you support?

All I had to say was, with an attempt at a suave, confident smile,

– I don't remember.

There was a helpful type called Richard who wore big glasses. In the dining hall, sitting near the blonde boy who was the best footballer and a big boy who called himself The Marshal and whose older brother was the toughest fighter in the school, Richard tried to offer me ways back to my forgotten truth.

– Is it Chelsea? Spurs? Man United? Arsenal? Everton? West Ham?

It was an awful moment. I managed to say to Richard, too quietly for the more glamorous boys to hear,

– Maybe Everton. I'll tell you tomorrow.

Richard assured me that Everton were good. Back at the desk I asked the nose-running boy what team he supported. He supported West Ham.

– You can support West Ham too. We're forever blowing bubbles.

It was a kind offer but I didn't trust his taste.

We lived above a dentist's surgery on a main road opposite Arnos Grove tube station. Our landlord was the dentist. He would find reasons to visit us sometimes and always behaved pleasantly but he made my mother very uncomfortable.

The landlord was fixing the heater in the bathroom. My sister made conversation with him. After he had gone, I asked my mother what football team I supported. She said she would call my uncle. My uncle had no interest in football himself but his son worked on a magazine called *Amateur Football*. The answer to my question was, I was told, Enfield. Enfield were perpetually top of the Isthmian League. I didn't smell a rat until the following day when I reported back to Richard.

He hadn't heard of Enfield. The Isthmian was an unimportant league played in by amateurs. I'd disappointed him. It was my first English failure.

I explained the situation to my mother. Together we pooled our football knowledge. There was something called the World Cup. The previous summer England had won the World Cup. This was a very good thing, which I, if I was to make my way in this new country, would have to know a lot more about.

– I'll get you a book, said my mother.

I had it the next day. I walked back from school part of the way with Stephen Moore, the blond boy who was the star footballer and who was, it was rumoured, related to Bobby, the captain of England. Stephen Moore was initiating me into the collecting of Captain Scarlet cards, which came from bubblegum packets, and which, if the whole set could ever be collected, formed a giant, magnificent jigsaw. I got back home, and after my mother and I fought over her disapproval of bubblegum (because it was bad for my teeth and because, like television, I wasn't allowed it because it represented America to her), she partly redeemed herself by presenting me with the book.

– I hope it's the right kind of thing, she said. It's a hardback, which means it will last.

The book was called the *Sportsview Book of Soccer*. It had cream-coloured hard covers that felt very good to the touch. It came from the second-hand shop and had a dignity and mystery about it. I ate my supper and read. It was dizzying.

The wounded hero of the book was John Charles, invariably called the gentle giant. John Charles was one of the greatest centre-forwards in the world. He was also one of the greatest centre-halves. Everything about him was strong and brave and skilful. His apotheosis in the *Sportsview Book of Soccer* comes when he plays for Wales in the World Cup quarter-final. He goes into the game with a broken arm and he plays at centre half, and he is magnificent, and Wales only lose 1-0, against the astonishing Brazil side, probably the most wonderful football team of history, better even than the 1954 Hungarians.

Brazil have Garrincha, 'the little bird', on the left wing, and they have Pelé in attack, seventeen years old, a prodigy. In the semi-finals they play their most difficult game, beating the second-best side in the tournament, France. The centre-forward of France is a charismatic man called Just Fontaine. Just Fontaine is an exile, like me, from Poland, like my absent father had been. Just Fontaine was the top scorer of the whole tournament, thirteen goals. He is wolfish and lethal.

England has Bobby Charlton. Charlton is nineteen with a grim old man's face. He's a survivor of the Munich Air Crash. (Two ghost sides are in the book: the Busby Babes of Manchester United who died in the crash, and the England side that might have been had they not.) Charlton was part of the England World Cup squad but never got a game. Why not? The *Sportsview* writers were appalled.

The *Sportsview Book of Soccer* was already my favourite book. The fact that it was about the 1958 season rather than 1966 was a matter for some original regret that quickly was forgotten. I took it into my bedroom, and I read it surreptitiously through much of the night.

It introduced me to a cosmology of heroes and a whole new language to describe them in. Goalkeepers were 'custodians' and the greatest was Lev Yashin of Russia, centre-halves always 'towered', wingers were 'mercurial', 'influential' inside-forwards played 'measured passes', and centre-forwards were (Just Fontaine apart) 'battering rams'.

The ultimate battering ram was Nat Lofthouse, the 'lion of Vienna', an Englishman with none of the Pole Fontaine's polish. He was a burly centre-forward 'in the classical mould', who scored the goals for Bolton Wanderers in the 1958 FA Cup Final. Bolton were playing Manchester United, rebuilt from the wreckage with survivors and veterans. Harry Gregg was the goalkeeper whom Lofthouse bundled over the line while holding the ball, a fair shoulder charge. Gregg's shoulder was dislocated by the collision but he had to play on. Maybe, the reporter speculated, one day substitutes might be allowed into the sport.

Sportsview writers enjoyed speculation and they applauded innovation. There was an admiring piece about Wally Barnes, the Arsenal full-back, who had devised his own method for dealing with opponents' throw-ins. He would stand directly in front of the player taking the throw, almost nose to nose, and then he'd jump up and down waving his arms. It had proved a very successful tactic. A lot of the subsequent throws were wild and went straight to Wally's teammates.

At school we had our own league going in lunchtimes and breaks. I was in the best team, captained by Stephen Moore. I wasn't a battering-ram in attack nor sufficiently wolfish, I couldn't go in goal because our custodian was the Marshal and he wasn't about to give up the position, so, because I was tall, I played centre-half, where I could tower. I was most effective at dealing with throw-ins. I had even improved upon Barnes's technique by shouting at the top of my voice and making faces while I jumped up and down with my arms flapping. I used the tactic in our playground league and I used it at the next organised football game until a teacher told me not to.

I got into my first proper fight because of Nat Lofthouse. Playground football, goals drawn on opposite brick walls. A corner, which I went up for. The ball bounced around, their goalkeeper (helpful Richard with the glasses) finally caught hold of it and the lion of Arnos Grove charged him, scrupulously fair, shoulder to shoulder. The ball spilled out of his hands and onto the wall shortly after Richard crashed into it, leading with his right arm and nose, bouncing off with his forehead, tumbling back against me already turning with a smile ready for the cheers. Richard's glasses were drooping off, they fell before he did, to the concrete, blood already seeping from nose; he landed there like a puddle and stayed.

Then The Marshal was attacking me and we were fighting, quite panicky and hard, until a teacher broke it up, and both of us were tugged away into the school building, through watching silent circles of schoolchildren who were looking at us as if we were dark and glamorous.

The Marshal had been Stephen Moore's best friend and now no longer was. Often I went round to Stephen Moore's flat to watch sport on tv with him and his father, something that The Marshal had used to do before I came on to the scene. On my side, I disapproved of The Marshal's school status, inflated by the fearsomeness of his brother. Also, The Marshal had beaten me out for the lead role in the Christmas play, and as the rehearsals went on he was showing what a bad decision that had been. Neither of us liked the other nor ever would, but both of us had secretly thought that we were going to lose the fight so there was an equal relief that it had been broken up, and The

Marshal often bullied Richard so his sudden defence of him was hypocritical at best.

So neither of us volunteered anything to the teachers, just mutely nodded when mute nods were being called for, until it was time to say thank you for being saved the pain of parents being called in, and we promised that we would never fight again. And then we were outside in the corridor again arguing over which of us should tell the others that football in the playground was not to be played with anything more exciting than a miniature plastic air ball for the next two weeks.

We stayed in the flat in Arnos Grove for about a year. I had learned enough. It was time to move on, and I wanted to stop supporting Manchester United. It was a half-hearted allegiance that had been born in *Sportsview*'s account of the horror of the Munich Air Crash but never really flourished. Taunts of 'Georgie Best, superstar, looks like a woman, and he wears a bra' didn't bother me. Alex Stepney conceding a goal to Pat Jennings when he let a long clearance by the Spurs goalkeeper bounce over his head in the Charity Shield did. Also, it was obviously wrong to support a team from another city. It was though a mystery to me at the time why we moved especially as the dentist (an Arsenal fan) told me he was lowering our rent.

By the time of the 1970 World Cup I was a football expert, a QPR supporter and a goalkeeper. The only mention of QPR in the *Sportsview Book of Soccer* is in a list of teams from the 3rd Division South. I discovered them for myself. I grew my hair like Rodney Marsh's and affected his part-deafness. As a goalkeeper I was sometimes brilliant, often awful, with a fastidious distaste for diving anywhere near dog shit.

I saved a penalty with my mouth once. This was a few years on, around the time of the 1974 World Cup, which England didn't qualify for. I wore braces then, so the ball was probably more at risk than my teeth, but all the same it was a proud swooping moment – into flight, sunshine, mud, squawking shouts, I dived too far, the ball thudded against my mouth and bounced away to safety. I wiped the blood away from my lips as my teammates jumped about around me.

I don't know if Gordon Banks ever saved a penalty with his mouth. He might have. He played a lot of games. He kept on playing even after he lost his right eye in an auto-accident. Perhaps then he saved a penalty with his mouth. Half blind, doing his best.

The flats where I lived in the summer of 1970 had a patch of grass out front where the boys from the neighbourhood played football and threw knives and discussed the England team. It was a mixture of Arsenal fans (the Irish), Spurs (the Jews) and Chelsea (Jews and Asians). I was the only QPR fan, which was maybe how I liked it. My patriotism was complicated and I enjoyed hearing the Irish boys slag off the England team. The Charltons were too old. Martin Peters was no good. Geoff Hurst had got lucky in one game and wasn't worth his place in a schoolboy side. Bobby Moore was a jewel thief who didn't know how to run. Gordon Banks was good. Everyone respected Gordon Banks. He was, it was agreed, the best goalkeeper in the world.

– Like Lev Yashin used to be, I said.

– Who? they said.

The only players to survive from the 1958 World Cup were Pelé and Bobby Charlton. Charlton had lost his hair; it was as if the rest of him had finally caught up with the age of his face. Pelé looked the same as he had always done. I had pictures of them, on stickers that we were all collecting in albums. One page for each team that had qualified for Mexico 1970. In the playground we swapped unnecessary Bulgarians for elusive Brazilians. Boy tycoons set the going rates. And at home we still didn't have a television set.

*   *   *

Sunday June 14, 1970. England against West Germany. Leon, Mexico. World Cup quarter-final. I was allowed with my sister to go to a neighbour's house and watch the first half only. My quisling sister was under strict instructions to bring me back at half-time.

I was nine. Gordon Banks was thirty. I watched the first half at Khalesh Patel's house. Gordon Banks watched the first half in the television lounge of the hotel in Leon. Neither of us saw the second half.

The game started. It didn't seem to matter that Gordon Banks had got food poisoning and was too sick to be in the game or even to travel to the stadium. My first glimmer of patriotism, this is maybe my country after all, we are playing very well, I could be part of this. Martin Peters scored a goal, Alan Mullery another. Everyone cheered, Hindus and Jews and Catholics, and I cheered amongst them. Although, I was interested to notice, a part of me wanted England to lose.

I don't know if there was a part of Gordon Banks that wanted England to lose. It would prove that the team wasn't good enough without him. I doubt it though. He seemed to be a proud rather than a vain man.

Gordon Banks, nursing his upset stomach, was watching the game on his own. The transmission was on tape delay. Maybe he took a sip from a glass of beer, listened to it enter his system without any obvious ill effect. He took another sip, rubbed his eyes, put the glass down on the table, stretched. He was nervous. A couple of waiters would have come in, asked him to sign his autograph. The waiters would probably have stayed in the TV room to watch the game with him, standing respectfully behind, hands behind backs, leaning against the wall.

Half time. England 2, West Germany 0.

– We have to go now, said my sister.

– We can't go now, I said.

– We have to go now, said my sister.

I couldn't bear the looks of compassion and contempt. We

walked back to the flat, past TV windows, over the patch of grass scattered with abandoned things, into the flats.

Gordon Banks cheered on the England team like I had done. Peter Bonetti seemed to be doing all right in goal. Alan Mullery scored. Alex Stepney, the other reserve goalkeeper, came into the TV lounge. We've lost the game, said Stepney. Banks laughed, returned his attention to the screen. Half-time. Banks stretched, the smiling waiter with the better English maybe asked him if he wanted another beer. Banks would have decided against it.

I went to my room. I took out the *Sportsview Book of Soccer*. Read again the accounts of the 1958 World Cup. In the quarter-finals Northern Ireland lost 4-0 to France (a hat-trick from Just Fontaine). Wales lost 1-0 to Brazil. England had been knocked out in the group stages, as had Scotland. My 1970 sticker book was still uncompleted. Nine stickers were missing. (There was a rumour going around that you could send in money to a certain address to get any missing stickers. This was agreed to be true, but no one knew the address.)

My mother came to my room to tell me it was time to switch the light off. My Rodney Marsh deafness prevented me from hearing her. I switched off the light as if it were my decision alone and curled beneath the covers. My mother kissed me on the forehead and closed the door softly behind her. I switched on the light again. England would play in the semi-finals now. Gordon Banks would be back for that game, which was a good thing. I liked Gordon Banks – not only was he the best goalkeeper in the world, there was something sad and stoical about his face.

It was still half-time on the delayed transmission when the England team returned to the hotel. The players told Banks they'd lost the game. He thought they were joking.

The Disappointed

DJ Taylor

South of Chelmsford they lost their way in a tangle of B roads and ended up in a lay-by looking at the map. The sun, dormant until now behind hedgerows, climbed suddenly into the sky and drenched the car's interior in blinding white light, so that, twisting round to look at him from the passenger seat, she could see only a glare of reflected surfaces, orange swirls and dense, aquarium shadows. Outside dragonflies bounced against the windows. 'Where are we?' she asked.

'Not far from Thorpe le Soken,' Douglas said. He was staring at the map with what she realised was a characteristic grimace: the way at any time over the last ten years he had stared at CD players that refused to function, documents that declined to yield up their intent: peevish, momentarily affronted, but innately confident in his own resourcefulness.

They cruised on for a while through fields of green sedge, eight-foot lanes engulfed by cow parsley. The smoke from Douglas's cigarette dribbled out of the wound-down window. In the distance grey stone rose beyond small, densely packed trees. The air was turning fresh.

'Where did Alain get this place anyway?'

'Some friend of his mother's. Just for the summer while he roughs out that treatment.'

There was an edge to the way Douglas said *treatment*. It was his usual way of referring to friends' accomplishments: Toby's *novel*; Greg's *first night*; Nick's *piece about Mrs Thatcher in the Economist*.

'Silly question, I suppose, but what are we going to do when we get there?'

'Watch it, of course.'

'Watch what?'

'Have you been living on Mars for the last fortnight? The football.'

Actually, Alexandra wanted to say as they negotiated a winding gravel drive, hemmed in by lofty rhododendrons, *I might just as well have been.* There was a weekend colour magazine lying in the pile of detritus at her feet with a picture of Gascoigne on the front and she picked it up and looked at it with faint incredulity. Once, not long ago, she had seen him on some lunch-hour chatshow and marvelled at, well, what exactly had she marvelled at? The absence of any kind of inner resource? The capitulation of everything – every question, every idea – before an overwhelming, bedrock chirpiness. He was like something out of a cartoon, she decided, every response hypertrophied into burlesque. How could you take him seriously, what he did seriously? Even more, how could you take seriously the people who were impressed or even just interested or amused by him?

Douglas's voice came floating through the ether. She realised guiltily, but not perhaps as guiltily as she might have done, that he'd probably been talking for a minute or more. ' . . . And so Roger said that what with all the arts supplements expanding and the *Independent* taking on people again, there was a good, no a *strong* chance, that . . .'

The gravel drive was thinning out now into not much more than a cart track. Great clumps of rhododendrons grew close to its edge, sometimes threatening to obliterate it altogether. Tipping her sunglasses back onto the bridge of her nose, she looked upward and found only inert grey sky, a plane tracking slowly along the horizon's edge.

'This is the real back of beyond,' Douglas said. He was turning faintly irritated now, she realised. 'Where did you put those directions?'

They pressed on through the rhododendrons until finally

the track swung left to meet a high flint wall. Slowly and incrementally the house took shape before them.

'It's quite something, isn't it?' Alexandra said. Together they contemplated the troughs and cornices of weathered, salmon-coloured brick. 'Almost *Brideshead*-y.'

'Of course,' Douglas said seriously. 'You have to realise that Alain could never actually afford to live somewhere like this. He can't earn more than twenty thousand a year.'

Which is more or less what you earn, Alexandra acknowledged. Another thought struck her. 'What's this girlfriend of Alain's called?'

'Claudia . . . No, Candia.'

'What does she do?'

'I don't know. Works for some newspaper.' Douglas looked at his watch. He was definitely cross about something, Alexandra divined, some lingering slight not yet confided to her. 'Come on. If we don't get a move on we're going to miss the opening ceremony.'

Later they had supper in a large white-walled kitchen with red tiles on the floor and a view out over rows of neatly planted apple trees. Cats came in through the open door and sat grooming themselves on the inner steps. Silent at the far end of the long oak table, Alexandra ate *salade niçoise* and French bread and listened to the football talk.

'Did you see that free kick against Egypt? And then Wright's header? *Magic.*'

'And Platt's one against Belgium? Gazza loops the ball over, he's got his back to goal, but he just turns round and *wham*!'

There were times, Alexandra thought, when it was possible to believe that all this knowledgeability, all this *expertise*, was wholly bogus, assumed in the same way one might put on a fashionable piece of clothing. People who knew about football, she suspected – and she knew nothing, she was happy to admit that – would trip the likes of Douglas up, overturn him and leave him sprawling on a mat of exposed limitations. She wondered if this was what was making her irritated – and she was irritated, she could feel annoyance rising in her like mercury – and decided that it was not the sound of Douglas and Alain talking about football, not even the faintly absurd and self-conscious attitudes they struck while they were doing it, but the long-term memory of their lavish but somehow unfocused enthusiasms. She remembered Douglas ten years ago in a college bar or a pub in North Oxford expounding some theory about pop music, something about Pink Floyd and punk rock, and almost bit her lip at the pain it caused her, all that ghosted seriousness about something which in the last resort you had no serious interest, the attitudes of a college tutorial taken out into real life.

Glancing along the table, she stared hard at the two of them in an attempt to work out what that decade had done to them. Made them more self-possessed? Less? Physically they seemed unchanged, or rather more defined. Ten years ago they had been clever middle-class teenagers moving confidently into their twenties. Now they were clever middle-class twenty-nine-year-olds moving a little less confidently into their thirties, spending a July evening in 1990 talking about the genius of Paul Gascoigne.

There was more food arriving now, bowls of fruit and yoghurt, and the movement made her shift her gaze. Candia, Alain's girlfriend, sat opposite and a little to one side: a plain, square girl of about twenty-five with what Alexandra had the nous to realise was a prohibitively expensive designer haircut, a kind of savagely inept Eton crop with tendrils escaping down her cheeks. Sphinx-like until now, Candia suddenly caught at something in the conversation and gave a tiny rap with her fork on the table top.

'That's interesting' she said. 'You just – forgive me if I didn't get it all – used the word *aesthetic* about this, this *game*. Now, allowing that the people playing it create something that can be described in these terms, how far do you think they're aware of what they're doing?'

'What do you mean?' Douglas asked.

'Well, what's his name? – Gascoigne? – scores a goal, let's say. Now, to you watching from the stand – well, from your armchair maybe – I can see that there's some pattern to it, some, well, *architecture*. But how do you think Gascoigne sees it?'

'Pure sensation,' Douglas said briskly. 'If you really want to know, I see Gascoigne as a kind of human racehorse. The beauty's all in the eye of the person beholding him. I mean, I don't see Gascoigne articulating it in any way, do you?'

'That might be an articulation problem, not a perception problem. Who can tell what Gascoigne thinks when he scores a goal?'

'He's a thick Geordie who left school at five or something. He'd probably be on the dole if he couldn't play football. I don't see the distinction.'

'And yet you admire him? I mean, all this stuff he does, it's an *achievement* of some kind?'

'Of course it is. How couldn't it be?'

'Thanks,' Candia said, 'I just wanted to know.'

Listening to this exchange, which struck her – at least on Candia's part – as angled or even premeditated in a way she could not quite comprehend, Alexandra found herself thinking of a boy in her primary school class called Gary Nichols. Coming from the middle-class end of a socially mixed collection of eight-year-olds, Alexandra had not exactly been forbidden to associate with the likes of Gary Nichols, but a certain amount of circumspection had been unobtrusively enjoined. She remembered, it would be difficult to say what she did remember. Gap teeth, certainly. An unfailing good humour in the face of what even at that age was a large amount of official asperity. Mild exhibitionistic tendencies. Chronically limited social repertoire. Oddly, Alexandra had rather liked him, even to the extent of inviting him to her ninth birthday party (he hadn't turned up), and had regretted his eventual departure to a special school on the other side of the city. But there was no doubt about it. In her eyes, Gascoigne and Gary Nichols had been forged in the same crucible.

Moving into the sitting room she heard Douglas saying, possibly to himself but perhaps to the room at large – as if there were some doubt about his fervour which he wanted to rebuke – 'We've got to win this one. We've just got to.'

'Why? Why have we got to win it?'

'It's Germany again. Like in 1966. 1970. Surely you can see the historical significance of playing Germany. I mean, surely you can remember what you were doing that day in 1966?'

'I burst into tears,' Alain said seriously. 'When Weber equalised. I threw myself on the floor and burst into tears.'

'My dad gave me a pound,' Douglas capped. 'Can you imagine? A whole pound.'

'I was five,' Alexandra volunteered. 'We must have been in Hong Kong. I don't remember anything about it.'

'1966,' said Candia, coming in through the doorway with a tray full of coffee mugs. 'I was in my cradle. What *is* it about this sporting nostalgia?'

Sitting in front of the widescreen TV, drinking coffee and smoking what Alain described as 'some high-grade Moroccan stuff, fresh off the boat', which Alexandra thought was incredibly juvenile but still consented to go along with, she heard that there were various preliminaries – warm-ups, handshakes, loudspeaker introductions – to be got through before the match began. Somehow this annoyed her even more, on one, abstract, level because it lashed a yet more complex and many-layered wrapper around the meagre kernel of these twenty-two hooligans kicking their ball about; more immediately because it gave Alain and Douglas a chance to proceed from the Football Talk and its lesser variant the Football Nostalgia Talk to what Alexandra always thought of as the Absent Friends Talk. Leaning back in her chair, watching the line of haggard, crop-haired men in white shirts being presented to a fat person in a blazer, she listened dreamily to the familiar fragments of rumour and disparagement.

' . . . Got fifteen thousand from Chatto & Windus, but Peter says he doesn't think he'll ever finish it.'

'Peter said that? If it was Peter he wouldn't even start it . . .'

' . . . When I last saw him he said the *Statesman* had stopped running his strip because they thought it was too depressing.'

'Oh it wasn't for that. Karl's never liked him since he used to go out with Julia at Cambridge . . .'

'Gracious,' said Candia. 'What a lot of people you seem to know.'

Fortunately this turned out to be an overture to Alexandra, and they had a companionable little gossip themselves about two or three mutual acquaintances dredged out of the world of print journalism and the TV fringes. Here Candia, whom direct questioning revealed as a researcher on *Newsnight*, proved so frighteningly knowledgeable that Alexandra felt rather non-plussed, like a veteran coach offering a work-out to some promising club athlete only to find herself unceremoniously steamrollered into the track. Lounging back in her chair again, as the figures crossed and recrossed on the fizzing screen, she felt suddenly chastened by the picture of herself that this conversation had thrown up, a kind of sadness in which, she realised, Douglas, Alain and the consciousness of past time each played their part. If, as occasionally happened, anyone asked Alexandra what she had been like at nineteen, she invariably smiled and offered only that 'I was very naive', something that Douglas – who had been the chief beneficiary of that naivety – always affected to find funny. In fact, Alexandra secretly thought she rather liked the nineteen-year-old she imagined herself to have been: innocuous, kind-hearted, docile. It pained her to think that she might be turning into one of those bright, brittle thirty-year-olds she had once regarded with such awe.

And contempt, of course. Something had happened onscreen, some player had keeled over or something, and Douglas was softly murmuring 'Bastard, bastard' under his breath. Alexandra couldn't tell whether he wanted this to be taken seriously, or whether it was part of the web of male complicity he and Alain were spinning over the evening.

'Butcher,' said Alain, with immense gravity, 'is amazing.'

'Totally amazing.'

'To take all that punishment and then just . . . get up.'

'Did you see him that time on the touchline after they'd carried him off? Before he had the stitches?'

They were a bit like an alternative comedy routine, Alexandra thought – not exactly funny, but encouraging the audience to despise their lack of self-awareness. For a moment, as the white phantoms surged back and forth over the green turf, she thought hard, very hard and seriously, about why she liked Douglas and decided – rather forlornly, for she had hoped that there might be other things that would leap out and surprise her – that it was to do with this lack of self-awareness. Somehow a Douglas who knew about his shortcomings and discussed them in the avid, guiltless way that people did on American talkshows would have been intolerable. In some ways, she decided, it was his ignorance of what he was that gave him charm.

It was nearly half-time. Alain and Candia were having a whispered conversation at the far end of the sofa. Talking to Alain, Alexandra saw, Candia's face grew animated in a way she had not previously noticed. Not certain whether she wanted more coffee or whether the proximity of other people was becoming irksome, she wandered slowly into the kitchen and sat down on one of the tall stools by the table. Here it was cooler and the light glinted off the surfaces to produce a sub-aqueous effect. Outside the first faint traces of dusk were falling over the garden and the fruit trees were gathered up in shadow. In the distance the sun burned off the hedgerows, and she stared out of the kitchen door into this curious, limpid world of shade and silence, motionless except for the birds noisily displacing each other from a rectangular table on the lawn. There was a disturbance behind her and Douglas came into the room carrying a beer glass.

'There's drink in the fridge if you want it.'

'No thanks.'

'They're doing really well, you know. I mean, they could score if they go on like this.'

'That's good then.'

Atmospheric subtleties had a habit of passing Douglas by. She had a memory of climbing with him up Siguraya Rock in Sri Lanka. Emerging onto the flat table of the summit, Alexandra had gasped at the tides of jungle – and at that height they seemed like a vast, undulating ocean – that spread out across the horizon. Douglas, arriving a few minutes later, the sweat coursing in rivulets over his forehead, had simply stared blankly around him: non-committal, faintly bewildered. Now, three years later in Essex, he rummaged in the fridge for a can of beer, straightened up and stood uncertainly looking at her.

'We could come and live somewhere like this,' he said. 'If you wanted to.'

'I thought you said you had to be in London for your work. I thought editors preferred sending the bikes to Highgate.'

'I don't know. We've been there eight years.'

'Jesus,' Alexandra said. 'Six months after we get a mortgage on a sodding flat, and you're talking about moving out of London.'

'I could write that book about MacLaren-Ross.'

'Yes,' she said, not unkindly. 'You could write that book about MacLaren-Ross. And I suppose when he hears about it the old bastard in Sussex who's sitting on the papers will give them to you out of sheer generosity.'

Douglas shrugged. He was, Alexandra knew, quite impervious to this kind of reasoning. Arguments in the flat at Highgate – which she suspected even now that they couldn't really afford – generally consisted of Alexandra shouting and Douglas shrugging, opening a can of beer, staring at her in a belligerent, slightly puzzled manner, rather, she thought, in the way he had examined the Sri Lankan jungle.

He looked at his watch. 'Second half,' he said. 'See you.'

Back in the sitting room the teams were out on the pitch again. Candia had stopped even pretending to take an interest and was reading a copy of *Possession*. Suddenly Alexandra heard Douglas say 'Good God, it's Tom!'

'What is?'

There was a copy of *Time Out* balanced on the lip of a magazine rack. Douglas seized it and threw it on the floor beneath the TV. 'That is. That's Tom.'

Looking at the upturned face, with its flat, regular features and garnish of fashionably short hair, Alexandra remembered being somewhere in Oxford, some party full of the dreadful people you saw at parties of that kind, people who acted in plays or worked on the magazines. People like her, she reflected uncomfortably.

'I thought you knew about Tom,' Alain said.

'I heard he was in films or something, but . . .'

'Oh, he's made it big all right.'

There was a roar from the screen. Alexandra watched the ball ballooning high off an outstretched leg and career into the net as a back-pedalling goalkeeper tried hopelessly to retrieve it.

'Fuck,' Douglas said. 'Fuck, fuck, fuck.' She knew, though, that half of him wasn't thinking about the football, was still, in fact, considering the question of Tom and Hollywood and a contract worth – Alexandra could dimly remember a story in the *Standard* now she thought about it – worth however many millions of dollars it was.

'That was some deflection,' Alain said authoritatively. 'Came off Parker.'

'What a wanker that bloke was,' Douglas said. 'I mean, do you remember him in tutorials? It was a miracle he ever got there in the first place. And then in finals – you're not going to believe this, Alex – we came out of the Political Thought paper, someone asked him about one of the set books, and it turned out he hadn't read *Leviathan*. Didn't even know what it was.'

'He used to go out with that Westmacott girl, didn't he?' Alexandra asked.

Douglas was doing fairly well, she thought, to pass all this off as amused exasperation or exasperated amusement. Watching him as he looked at Alain, who stared back rather worriedly, she could see he was making a conspicuous effort to control himself.

'A date with Helen Westmacott? They used to call her ex-boyfriends the potholing and mountaineering club.'

'Don't think me rude or anything,' said Candia from the sofa, 'but will you stop going on about Tom. Only he happens to be rather a friend of mine.'

'A friend of *yours*?'

'That's right. A friend of mine. So will you please stop going on about him?'

'Candy . . .' Alain began.

'Hey,' Douglas said. Alexandra still couldn't tell whether he was seriously angry, or still humorously exasperated. 'I grew up with Tom Newsome. And I think I can say whether he's a wanker or not.'

'I think growing up's putting it a bit charitably, don't you?' Candia said. 'Look, let's put it another way. Will you please stop laying down the law on things you know hardly anything about? We had Mrs Thatcher at supper. Now it's Tom Newsome. I suppose after this stupid football match it'll be government fiscal policy or something.'

There was another bellow from the screen. 'Lineker,' Alain said anxiously. 'Equalizer.'

Alexandra stared wonderingly around the room: at Douglas, who was silently opening and closing his mouth; Alain, half turned to the TV screen; Candia, who had gone white in the face and was drumming her fingers against the cover of her book.

'I'm sorry,' she said. 'You're going to have to excuse me.'

They watched her go. On the screen the white figures danced, re-grouped, broke apart.

'Ex-boyfriend,' Alain said. 'Sorry. Should have told you.'

'Even so.'

'Even so. Exactly.'

'One all,' Alain said after a while. 'Anything could happen.'

Much later – at one or two in the morning – they went to bed in a high, oak-panelled room looking out over the inky lawn. 'I'm so disappointed,' Douglas kept saying, as he tossed his clothes item by item onto the bedside table. 'Bloody Pearce, just hacking it like that. I mean, what do we pay them for?' Looking at him as he lurked at the foot of the bed, ribcage gleaming in the sharp light, shirt tugged over his head, Alexandra thought that he wasn't in the least moved. Something else struck her about the low, sluggish rhythm of the day and she said:

'Why didn't you tell me Macmillans had turned your book down?'

He blinked for a second, weighing up his response. 'Because it doesn't matter. Someone else will take it. It just doesn't matter.'

It would always be like this, Alexandra supposed: her watching him summon the strength to cast off these rebuffs, forever standing there flushed, irritated but finally invulnerable. She twisted slightly in the bed as he slumped down beside her, thinking for some reason of Gary Nichols' farmboy grin, her nineteen-year-old self stepping timorously through the college quadrangles. 'I'm so disappointed,' Douglas muttered again into the pillow at her side.

'So am I,' she said.

Some of My Best Friends Are German

Dave Rimmer

Visiting Berlin while the Germany-Portugal qualifier for France
'98 is being played at the Olympiastadion, I end up watching the
game on TV with a bunch of old cronies across town. One of them
walks in late.

'Who's playing?' he asks. 'Helmer?'

'Helmer,' I concur, then start reeling off other names in a
kind of bored and monotonous chant. 'Helm-er . . . Hässl-er . . .
Basl-er . . .'

Others laugh and join in.

'Kohl-er . . . Reut-er . . . Zieg-e . . .'

The joke lumbers on through the game along with cracks
about Klinsmann's manifest inability to break his international
goal drought and speculation about just what kind of car French
ref Monsieur Batta can expect as a bung from the German
authorities. 'BMW!' someone shouts, as Portugal's Rui Costa
gets booked. 'Opel Manta!' another admonishes, as Bierhoff is
judged offside. And when, in the 76th minute – just five minutes
after Barbosa scores for Portugal to take the lead – Rui Costa gets
a red card for the second bookable offence of not leaving the field
quickly enough when substituted, everyone begins a chorus of
'MER-CED-ES!! MER-CED-ES!!'

In truth I can't remember too much more about the game,
except for a general sense that at that point Portugal were
outplaying Germany and deserved to win. My German friends
seemed to agree and, jokes aside, were shaking heads in befuddle-
ment at the harshness of Rui Costa's sending-off. But hey! – they
can afford to be magnanimous. In the whole history of the World
Cup, Germany have only ever lost one qualifying game, and that

was back in 1985 (although, promisingly, it was to Portugal). They even find it funny that I'm sitting there among them, furiously willing their team to lose.

Someone stabs the remote and we switch to a channel that's offering the same game but with Portuguese commentary. All we can hear is:

'Reut-er . . . Zieg-e . . . Hässl-er . . . Köpk-e . . .'

So anyway, yes, some of my best friends are German – a statement I mean both as literal truth, and with all the irony that formulation allows. I lived in Berlin for many years, and though I don't want to live there any more, no city on earth feels more like home. I've fallen in love with Germans, travelled with Germans, drunk and danced and laughed and watched football with Germans. And I've cried on German shoulders, more than once.

Yeah, and some of the people I hate the most are German, too, but at least this is because I've got to know them. In my childhood Germans were unambiguously The Enemy. Bad eggs, the lot of 'em! My aged Grandpa, slowly expiring upstairs, had been wounded in the trenches. The top of an old chest of drawers in the attic had been splintered by falling masonry during the Blitz. Television constantly screened old movies full of heroic Brits and snarling Nazis. Me and my pals ran round the nearby woods playing Jerries and English, pointing sticks at each other and making staccato, machine-gun noises. I was ten years old in 1966. Victory seemed right and proper.

Despite having prevailed at just about every encounter over the three intervening decades, Germans still nurse a sense of outrage about the 'cheating third goal'. But it does seem to me that West Germans of my generation have come to deal with the past a lot better than their English equivalents, many of whom might as well be still be running around with sticks going rat-a-tat-tat-a-tat-tat! Of course there are knobheads in every nation (and an extra-specially large amount of them in the former East Germany) but I still can't imagine Germans taking revenge for a World Cup upset by torching English cars in the street – even if only because they'd be hard pushed to find any.

I watched most of Italia '90 in the back room of the Pinguin Club, a West Berlin bar where I sometimes worked. Earlier that year, on the night of the first East German elections, I'd messed around with Jägermeister, orange juice and other ingredients and finally came up with a layered drink in the colours of the German flag – the Einheitscocktail, 'Unity cocktail'. We'd give it away free at Great Moments in History, which cropped up that year like clockwork. Yes, went the joke as our customers grimaced – for the thing tasted truly disgusting – it's just like German unity: really complicated to put together, really expensive, and when you've finished, it makes you sick.

To live in Berlin at that time was to watch the old order quite literally collapsing around you. We'd talk politics and history deep into the night. Everyone was worried about resurgent nationalism, and the effect that a German World Cup victory might have. In the end, though, German friends would quite reasonably shrug and admit: 'But I still want us to win, because that's my team.'

And of course I felt the same about England, wobbling their way towards the semi-final. The Cameroon tie came just a couple of days after currency union and the last gasp of the East German economy. The day of the semi-final against Germany found me flying to England on family business. I caught most of the first half between planes at Schiphol airport. On the next plane, the captain kept us up with the score. 'We're now flying at 33,000 feet – and Lineker has just equalised!' Right in the middle of the penalty shoot-out, seconds after Pearce fluffed it, we landed and the captain went silent. Everyone dashed out of the plane and into the terminal, looking to left and right. No TV. No nothing. My dad was there to pick me up, and we raced back to my parents' house. On the doorstep stood my mother, who silently shook her head.

*   *   *

Back in London for Euro '96, I called up the Pinguin before the semi-final. They laughed: 'We were just thinking of calling you too!' I called them later from a payphone in a pub, drunk and a little deflated. They were gracious and sympathetic: 'It should have been the Final, Dave, just like it should have been in 1990.'

But something along the way has changed. I've always known one or two Germans who just can't abide the national team. 'Everything that's wrong with Germany,' they'll mutter. 'Organisation and system to the exclusion of personality and flair.'

'I don't understand it, really,' moaned one German friend in the Pinguin some time after Euro '96. 'We're not South Korea. We're not China. We're not a nation of robots.'

I had to laugh at this point, and we launched into a lively discussion about international perceptions of Germany. Soon it was back to football, though. 'Ince!' my friend enthused. 'Shearer! Gascoigne! Fantastic! What a character! Why don't we have players like these?'

Instead they have: 'Kohl-er . . . Basl-er . . . Helm-er . . . Hässl-er . . .'

After Rui Costa's dismissal, the Portuguese manager has to pull off someone else to bring on the player he wants. Somewhere in the reshuffle, they lost whoever was supposed to be shadowing Ulf Kirsten, Germany's answer to Desperate Dan. In the 81st minute he scores with a typically artless, thundering headlong charge of a goal. Portugal are almost certainly out. Germany, with only Armenia and Albania to face, are almost certainly through. And though everyone acknowledges it was a lacklustre performance, not one of my friends is arguing with success.

As Seen on Radio

Graham Joyce

The radio drifted out of frequency just as something was happening, so I slapped Billy hard on the ear. Communications Theory suggests that a radio signal will not distort during a period in which nothing worthwhile is said. Right then something critical and historical was happening, so the frequency drifted, the radio fuzzed and spat, and brother Billy was perfectly positioned for a slap.

I got up and looked out of the window but, seeing no sign of the pair of them, I sat down and chewed my fist. The Hun meanwhile had a direct free-kick on the edge of our box after Nobby Stiles impeded Uwe Seeler, the Mercedes-Benz of German football, with a commando-style chop to the throat. The Hun protested vigorously but what did they expect? This was Wembley! England was the birthplace of soccer, and no sausage-guzzling Hun was going to filch the glittering winged goddess from under our noses without earning a bruise or two.

So while Seeler massaged his throat and Billy nursed his ear, Haller stepped up to take the kick and the radio went into broadcast spasm. Something had happened. Had the Hun equalised? Surely not. Mere minutes remained before Bobby Moore would claim, kiss and hold aloft the winged goddess. I scrambled to my feet to look out of the window again, but there was still no sign of Tony and Frances.

'Why do you keep looking out of the window?' Billy spat. I showed him a dipping backhand and he ducked sharply to avoid a second slap. 'Don't hit me!' he shouted. 'Why did you hit me?'

'You moved!' I roared. 'Don't move!'

If anyone got up and walked past the table on which the feeble transistor radio was perched the radio produced a belch of static followed by a frequency drift in which some presumably fat mezzo-soprano bitch mouthing Verdi on a neighbouring station would invade the airwaves for three seconds. It was maddening. I assumed the fact that we were at the coast didn't help, what with the bracing wind blowing radio commentary about like washing on a line, so I'd insisted that nobody move. This was my big mistake. It gave Tony and Frances an excuse to go outside. Together.

What's more, with Billy and me huddled like chess players over the table, the radio still managed, every few minutes, another frequency drift. 'I didn't!' Billy protested. 'I didn't move!'

'You moved,' I shouted, 'before the kick was taken!' I admit I confused myself with this one, somehow conflating a football technicality with dimwit notions of how radio waves operate.

I glared out of the window again. The radio commentator indicated that the referee was studying his watch. Seconds remained. England were moments away from lifting the Jules Rimet trophy. The glittering goddess was already making her docking descent from the blue skies over Wembley, gently enfolding her wings about the stadium, bathing the 97,000 crowd in effulgent light. Then, just as I glimpsed Tony and Frances sitting together on the sea-wall, the Hun smacked in their ninetieth-minute equaliser. The startled goddess instantly recoiled back into the heavens, leaving an eerie chill in her wake.

Billy shrank back in his seat, anticipating another hot ear.

It was June 30th 1966 and the universe was out of joint. Every soccer fan in the country (how I hated that word 'fan' with its implied levity when the correct terms of allegiance were praetorian, bloodletting, terrorist in their passion) was nailed to a TV set and I was in Rhyl, North Wales, listening to the World Cup final on poxy radio. Why? Because I was thirteen years old, and as every thirteen-year-old knows, thirteen is shit.

We had a television all right, but at home. It wasn't poverty that had driven me to the desperate straits of gluing an ear to the weak signal coming from a battered, whistling little Hitachi plastic box. It was the Industrial Fortnight. What perverse calendar, what grievous timetabling could intersect the apotheosis of English football with the diktat of the Industrial Fortnight?

'Industrial Fo'tnight,' said my old man, hanging up his cloth cap after work one evening. 'That's why.'

I couldn't believe it. This was his answer to the question of why we were about to take our annual seaside holiday at the same time as the World Cup finals. His only answer. There he was, still reeking of the paint-shop from the Coventry Chrysler assembly-line, casually tucking into his egg, sausage and chips as if everything was normal. My eight-year-old brother Billy, also a keen football fan, sat opposite gloomily munching on a chip sandwich. He too was disappointed, but unlike Billy I felt the decent half of an Oedipal rage. I wanted to knife my old man. I wanted to eviscerate him. Turn over his chariot and hurl it down the ravine. All of that. At that precise moment I hated him: the stink of paint; his cloth-cap; and most of all his relentlessly cheerful industrial manner. He didn't get it. This lumpen prole who had never kicked a ball in anger and who smothered his plate in brown sauce just didn't get it.

'What's up with you?' he said genially, looking up from his sausage. 'You look as if the parrot just died.'

I couldn't speak. I went out, slamming the door behind me. I heard him say, 'Teenagers!', in a grunt followed by the sound of him smacking the arse-end of a sauce bottle with the flat of his hand.

After identifying the problem, the old man told me to cheer up, assuring me they'd find a place with a TV somewhere, and that if the worst came to the worst he knew a pub across the road from the holiday camp and and and . . . by which time I'd passed the entire coach journey from Coventry to Rhyl wearing a designer-sneer the shape of the Horseshoe Pass.

On the first day of the fortnight at the Golden Sands Holiday Camp I escaped the chalet accommodation with considerable vim. 'Can I come?' said Billy.

'No.'

Billy, who every day would have followed me into the slavering jaws of teenage hell, looked hurt and dejected. I relented. 'All right, but you walk behind me and you don't say anything.'

We stood in communal misery on the concrete sea-wall, looking at the whitecaps far out to sea. The sky was overcast and the shingle beach was empty. A grey-backed gull hovered over the breakers, riding the thermals while the stiff breeze whipped at my nylon wind-cheater and squeezed moisture from my eyes.

'Permission to speak,' Billy said. After a suitable pause I nodded. Billy gestured along the wall at another youth some twenty yards away. Shoulders slumped and hands thrust in his pockets, the youth was gently booting the sea-wall. He looked as pissed off as I was. 'We should say hello,' Billy suggested, 'and form a gang.'

I grabbed Billy by the collar, tightening it round his windpipe. 'Listen. I don't want a gang. So don't mention gangs to me again, right?'

'Keep your wig on,' Billy said, flushed, red-faced, straightening his collar.

I looked along the wall at the boy. In many ways he was my mirror image. Same jeans, same nylon wind-cheater. Same Horseshoe Pass scowl. 'Come on then. And keep your mouth shut at all times.'

The boy's name was Tony, and he was equally burned up about being dragged away from the World Cup Final and the impending collapse of the Hun. We had a lot in common. We kicked the wall together; we played Who Do You Know In Coventry. Wild times. Occasionally Tony would glance at the muted Billy and say, from the side of his mouth, 'Doesn't speak much, does he?'

He had this habit, Tony, of speaking out of the corner of his mouth while darting a glance over his shoulder, as if an enemy might be lurking nearby. He was the same age as me but he behaved like someone who'd spent years in Alcatraz.

'No, but he's a good kid,' I felt obliged to answer, and for which Billy was pathetically, gurglingly grateful. And what's more, he'd got his gang.

On the second day Billy inducted Frances into his gang. I don't know what Frances, fourteen, was doing talking to Billy, eight, but I spotted the pair of them leaning against the sea-wall, gazing out at the ocean. Billy had developed an intuitive knack of knowing when I was coming up behind him: he always skittered back a few paces as if to avoid an imminent blow to the head. 'This is Frances,' he blurted, 'and she's got no one to play with. Will you and Tony play with her?'

Frances and I exchanged glances and smiled at Billy like indulgent grandparents, though I would have liked to knuckle his head. 'I didn't say that,' Frances said, tucking a strand of hair behind her ear. 'I said there weren't many people here of my own age.'

She was right. The Golden Sands Holiday Park, with its barracks-style wooden chalets and its rustbucket caravans fairly bustled with cricketing boys and little girls who carried plastic lilos everywhere; there were pensioners snoozing in deck chairs; women who stood around all day with curlers in their hair and a fag burning; dads flying kites for their kids; there were sandcastle competitions and crazy-golf and a penny arcade and bingo evenings. But no TV room, and no other teenagers, and nothing for teenagers to do.

'At least I know you now,' said Frances. The breeze whipped at her fine brown hair, and she peeped at me through her fringe in a way that gave me an unfamiliar jolt. She made me feel worth knowing. She made me feel like I counted for something.

'And there's Tony,' I said, 'so that makes three of us.'

Billy blinked pathetically. 'Four counting Billy,' Frances said. I peered at Billy as if he was one of the plate-sized jellyfish washed up on the beach. She seemed to read my mind. 'Got to count Billy. After all, without him we wouldn't be able to play together.'

'Yeh,' I said. 'He's all right.' I don't know why I was telling everyone he was all right. In fact he was a pesky little vexation to the spirit who wouldn't stop shadowing me. But Frances somehow made me generously disposed. I took a swipe at him to show it, but he danced out of range. Then I remembered something. 'Don't suppose you like football, do you?'

She wrinkled a finely freckled nose. 'Don't suppose I do.'

She was pretty, I decided, though her deep brown eyes searching me from behind her untamed fringe kept me on edge. Frances suggested a walk along the sea front towards the town. We set off. Billy followed a few paces behind, lobbing pebbles onto the shingle beach. The sun flirted between clouds. It was a few miles into town, but it gave me the opportunity to explain to Frances how England, if they could overcome Portugal and the goal-scoring prowess of Eusebio, would probably come up against West Germany in the final, who in turn should have no problem in disposing of the Russians, Yashin the legendary 'cat' goalkeeper in black notwithstanding.

Frances was terrific. She took it all in. 'Eusebio and the cat,' she said. Then she moistened her lips with her tongue. 'Eusebio and the cat.'

I liked her a lot. I liked her wry sense of humour. She had what I would later come to understand as a genius for enlarging any ordinary moment, so that a walk along the sea front became an excursion; a paddle in the water became an event. You could try to repeat these things in her absence, but they would never be the same. She had that endearing habit of delicately lifting a stray lock of hair with her index finger and parking it behind her ear. Plus she would listen endlessly about football.

I introduced her to Tony later that day, and I could tell that Tony liked her too. For the next few days we were inseparable, and Billy too was never far behind, as Frances taught us the latent art of dossing; of having a terrific time doing absolutely nothing.

She could do nothing with immense style, and it seemed to me that during these sequences of nothingness she brought us to the very wall of experience. We lolled on the concrete tidal barrier for hours; we ambled into town just to turn around and come back again; we tossed pebbles at tin cans. It was easily the best holiday I'd ever had.

'Frances is great, isn't she?' Tony said to me, in her absence, out of the side of his mouth.

'Yep,' I said. 'Yep.'

The semi-final came around and England took on the plucky Portuguese. There had been loose talk of us watching the match in a local pub. My old man had indeed located a pub with a TV set, rare in those days, but the landlord refused children admission. Dad, to his credit, told the landlord he was a miserable bastard; the remark only galvanised the landlord into posting a notice on the door:

STRIKLY NO UNDER-AGE

I poured scorn on the illiterate landlord. In fact I went on about his illiteracy for hours on end until Tony, squirting the words from the side of his mouth, said, 'Give it a rest, will you?'

It was Frances who produced the transistor radio. She used to leave it on the beach wall of an evening, tuned to Radio Caroline. 'You three listen to the match. I'm going into town for the afternoon,' she said. We accepted the tinny tranny with bad grace.

It wasn't a great game. The signal on the radio kept drifting out. At half-time Tony said, 'Wonder what Frances is doing now?' But the important thing was that England won. Germany too saw off the Russians, as I'd predicted. The battle lines were drawn. We were on our own again. It was just us versus the Hun.

'Why do you call them the Hun?' Frances asked me.

'Germans. Krauts. Hun.'

'Never heard that before.'

'You must be thick. Heard that before haven't you Tony?'

'Not before you said it,' he quipped, glancing behind him.

I decided Tony was just taking her side. Anyway, it didn't matter what you called them; Monty versus Rommell, Roller versus Merc, the insouciant and indomitable English character against the steely organisation and discipline of the German machine, with the Jules Rimet trophy as the gleaming prize.

That trophy. That magnificent Deco winged cup, sadly withdrawn from the tournament after Brazil clinched their third triumph to take it outright. Mourn its loss, that solid gold figurine goddess, wings at full pinion, arms aloft in a graceful rapture of victory, bearing the grail volant. The artefact itself only beautiful, merely holy, a precise emblem of the soaring spirit infecting the stadium at the moment of victory. Not like that messy, melting bauble they knocked up to replace it.

In the couple of days that followed I got caught up in a slow-motion scramble. I guess it had been going on since the first day I met Frances, but I hadn't noticed. Yet it happened with the invisible but slow certainty of a stalagmite forming on a cave floor. Somehow the distance between Frances and Tony and Frances and me was shrinking. I'm not referring to the psychological or emotional distance or any other abstract thing; I'm talking about the physical distance between our bodies, the measurable reach. It was closing at the rate of a centimetre per hour, for both Tony and I. I didn't realise it until I was able, one evening, to smell the shampoo on Frances's hair; and on that same evening I noticed how the crisp fold of Tony's shirt sleeve brushed the shoulder of her jacket. Tony and I were in a frozen but melting dash to stand as close to Frances as possible. And the nearer we came to closing it, the more the gap came to ache like an open wound.

With Billy abed the three of us sat out at night as long as we dared, perched on the sea-wall, legs dangling in the dark, watching the eerie blue phosphorescence of the waves and listening to the weak signal of Radio Caroline. Fortunately it was always Frances who had to return to her chalet first, so we were never put to the test of defying parental decree by staying out too late.

It didn't matter, since we found other ways to compete. Frances had a terrific laugh, one that would seize and fold her entire body, so humour was at breaking point. Inevitably Tony made some remark about the size of my nose or maybe I made a comment about how his ears stuck out. The banter escalated rapidly and started to take on a nasty edge. We were still slinging abuse when Frances jumped down from the wall and snapped off her transistor radio.

'I'm off. See you both in the morning. 'Night.'

We were left to gaze after her in silence. In the dark behind us a wave dashed itself on the shingle.

We sat there sullenly for a while, out of conversation. It seemed pointless to be there without Frances. 'I'm gonna hit the sack,' I said.

'Yeh,' said Tony, but he stayed there as I made my way back to the chalets.

The next morning was sunny and the sea was calm. I found Frances at our usual sea-wall rendez-vous spot under the ramp affording access to the beach. She gazed steadily out to sea, hardly seeming to notice as I settled beside her. Suddenly she leapt up on to the shingle. 'Come on,' she called over her shoulder, 'we're going into town.'

By the time I caught up with her she'd taken off her pumps and socks and was paddling in the water where the shingle became sand. 'What about Tony?' I said. We'd had a tacit agreement to meet every morning at the same time.

'I saw him on my way. He's going to Conway castle with his Mum and Dad.'

Conway castle? This sounded odd. No one over the age of ten goes to Conway castle with their Mum and Dad, and I said so. But I wasn't complaining. It meant I had the entire morning alone with Frances. Or so I thought. We hadn't gone more than two hundred yards when someone came up behind us, skimming flat pebbles across the water.

'Billy!' Frances said. 'Coming into town with us?'

'Can I?' He looked at me, dewy-eyed.

I must have stood there for a long time, my features frozen between a smile and a scowl. I was trying to make a decision. I had exactly five shillings in my pocket, in two coins. Finally I withdrew one of the half-crowns and offered it to Billy. 'Go and have some fun on the slot machines,' I said, with film-star largesse.

Billy stared at the silver cartwheel in my hand. He was speechless and yet he couldn't disguise the quizzical light in his eye. A half-crown was a glittering fortune to an eight-year-old. He took it from my hand, and for one ridiculous moment I thought he was going to test the coin by biting it. Then he ran full speed up the beach, presumably before I could change my mind.

'Why did you do that?' Frances said after we'd gone a little further.

I shrugged it off. 'He'd just be bored with us.'

'You are so good to your kid brother,' Frances said. 'So good.'

I had to look at her to see if she was taking the piss. She wasn't. She actually thought I'd given the kid half my money just out of the milk of human kindness.

'I hate it when you and Tony bicker,' she said suddenly. 'Why do you do that?'

I picked up a round flat pebble and threw it into the sea. 'It's just a laugh.'

'Is it?'

Somewhere along the beach I found a stick of driftwood and I wrote her name in the wet sand, in burning ten-foot-high letters. She took the stick off me and sketched a huge heart. But inside it she wrote

Frances

lovs

?

I didn't like the bottom line. 'Where's the E?'

'What?'

'The E. The E.' She looked blankly at the huge heart carved in the sand. Then it dawned on me that Frances couldn't spell. 'Thick or what?' I heard myself digging. 'Not exactly a big word is it? God if you can't spell that you must be a bit dense.' Frances coloured, gazing down at her mistake. I might have left it at that but it seemed I couldn't. 'You must have been in the queue with that landlord when they gave out the brains.'

Scattering shingle, Frances turned on her heels and walked up the beach, arms folded tightly.

I was furious with myself. I couldn't understand what perversity of my own nature had me mouthing off in that way. My first opportunity to be alone with Frances and I'd blown it. I hurried after her. 'Sorry.'

She squinted into the stiff, salty wind. 'It's OK.'

But it wasn't. Though we carried on walking towards the town, the wind had changed. We went to the funfair and had a ride on the dodgems. I stepped up to the rifle range and won a plastic replica of the Jules Rimet trophy, its gold varnish peeling even before it fell into my hands. A peddler was selling cheap identity bracelets on the sea-front and I spent the last of my money on one for Frances, engraved with her name; but even that didn't make it right. We caught the bus back to the Golden Sands, and she paid.

The next day was the afternoon of the final. My folks were out on the beach with their flask and sandwiches as Tony, Billy, Frances and I assembled in our chalet to listen to the live commentary on Frances's transistor radio. Even Frances had been unable to resist the mounting national hysteria. Though it was the middle of summer, and we were indoors, Billy wore his wool-knitted England hat and scarf. Some of the chalets paraded home-made bunting and good luck messages to the

England team. And anyway, Frances said, she wanted to hear about 'Eusebio the cat'.

'Tell her,' I said wearily.

'You tell her,' Tony retorted, still smarting over the fact that Frances and I had spent time together without him. It emerged he hadn't been to Conway castle at all, but I didn't tell him Frances had lied.

It fell to Billy to explain to Frances that the chances of either the Portuguese striker or the Russian goalkeeper figuring in an England versus Germany World Cup Final were slim; though he managed to make it sound as if Frances had cleverly come up with an intriguing proposition.

The game was about to get underway when Tony observed that whatever the result he couldn't really lose. I asked him what he meant.

'My Dad's German,' he said. 'He was a prisoner-of-war. He stayed in this country after the war.'

I didn't like the sound of this at all. When invited to a hanging one doesn't want to be seated with relatives of the condemned man. 'But your Mum's English?' I insisted.

'Oh yeh.'

'And you were brought up in this country?'

'Oh yeh.'

He wanted England to win, he assured us, but his own father would be pleased if the result went the other way. The game started and the Wembley roar crackled over the radio. I was beginning to have serious doubts about Tony, but after twelve minutes we were all holding our heads as Haller neatly slotted one in for the Hun. Six minutes later we were dancing, Tony included, as Hurst pulled one back. You can say what you like about football but if nothing else it encourages young men to hug each other. At half-time it was honours-even, and Frances announced she was going for a walk.

A few seconds later Tony said, 'Gonna stretch my legs,' and followed her out.

Billy was studying me carefully. I stared at the wall, pretending to listen to the half-time pundits, but hearing nothing. 'D'you think we'll win?' Billy said meekly.

I scowled. 'Maybe. Maybe not.'

After the restart Tony and Frances returned together. No one said anything. Then with twelve minutes to go, Martin Peters seemed to win the game for England. More ecstatic hugging. We ran out of the chalet, and we ran back in again as the Hun began a ferocious bombardment of the England goal. Time crystallised.

'I can't stand the suspense!' Frances cried after a few more minutes, and she went out again.

'Me neither,' said Tony, and he trailed after her for the second time. It was only a few moments later, when Billy asked me why I kept looking out of the window, that I gave him a slap. Right at the death of the game I looked out to see Tony and Frances sitting on the sea-wall, holding hands; and the Hun equalised.

I went outside and promptly vomited. When I returned, Billy was in tears.

Perhaps Frances and Tony, out there on the sea-wall, got wind of what was happening because they came back, slightly red-faced, just before the game was restarted for extra-time. Frances gave Billy a hug.

'Don't worry Billy,' I said, baring my teeth and trying to muster an optimism I didn't feel. 'The Hun won't cope with the strength-sapping Wembley turf. You'll see.'

Billy had an almost biblical faith in everything I told him, and he looked at me with shining, wet eyes. But perhaps I was right for once. England launched themselves at the Germans with an unexpected frenzy. Alan Ball in particular injected demented energy down the right flank, and it was his inch-perfect cross, in the eleventh minute of extra time, that found Geoff Hurst poaching just outside the German six-yard box.

What happened next has been the subject of endless debate, dissection, review, mythologising, literary reference and even preposterous mathematical computer analysis of the width of the white goal-line in relation to the diameter of the ball. To this day the Hun still dispute the Hurst goal. But all we cared about was that England had popped in the winner. The radio commentator reported the German dispute and the agonising consultation between referee and Russian linesman, but the goal stood.

After the delirium subsided the commentator was still speculating about the controversial goal. 'What are they on about?' I sneered. 'It was obvious the ball crossed the line.'

'Anybody could tell that,' Billy agreed.

'A Hun trick,' I said.

'Hang on,' Frances objected. 'How do you know for sure?'

I dismissed her with a wave. 'Anybody could tell.'

'How? How exactly could you tell the ball crossed the line when you only heard it on the radio?'

I made a swatting motion. 'Hushh!'

Play moved into the final nail-biting segment. It was excruciating as the Hun flung everything forward in a last-ditch effort to come on terms. Panic crept into England's defending as they tried to hang on. But Frances wasn't letting the matter drop. It was bad enough with the radio drifting in and out of frequency without her loudly demanding to know how anyone could tell that the ball had crossed the line from a radio account.

My patience snapped. 'What do you know about football?' I shouted.

Then Tony intervened. His voice had a strange curve. 'She's got a point. How can you tell, when you didn't see anything? You only know what you've been told. You didn't see anything.'

There was a sickening hiatus as I tried to think my way out.

'A Hun trick,' Billy said, trying to come to my aid.

'Backspin,' I tried desperately. 'If you know anything at all about football you'll know that a ball coming off a bar can gather backspin and bounce out.'

Tony wasn't letting me off the hook. 'But you couldn't see that. On radio.'

I waved him away and turned up the volume in anticipation of the roar of the capacity Wembley crowd, staring hard at the plastic radio, willing the referee to blow his whistle. Then in the dying seconds Hurst put the matter beyond all doubt. I hugged Billy, and while he and I were dancing I sensed the door open and someone go out. The radio signal spat, fuzzed, drifted and returned to audial clarity as the Jules Rimet goddess enfolded her glittering wings about the Wembley throng. I looked around for Frances but she'd gone, and Tony had too.

For the rest of the holiday I saw very little of Frances and Tony. They seemed to keep out of my way. Occasionally I spotted them walking along the beach together, but they stopped hanging around the sea-wall.

I still had Frances's transistor radio, and I was determined to return it to her. One evening I spotted them in the twilight, up by the sea-wall. But by the time I'd hurried back to the chalet and returned with the radio they were locked in an embrace and kissing. I stood watching for a few moments, fumbling with the tuner-dial on the radio, but they were oblivious to my presence.

On the last but one day of the holiday, Billy and I were standing at the sea's edge. Billy was skimming flat stones across the water when Frances and Tony walked by, arm in arm, she resting her head on his shoulder.

Either they didn't see, or they preferred to ignore us. I stared at their diminishing backs as they walked along the water's edge, and I was hurt by the depth of their affections for each other. Then I felt Billy tugging insistently at my sleeve. 'Just think about it,' he said. 'We won the World Cup.'

The Battle of Santiago

Ben Richards

Good Evening. The game you're about to see is the most stupid, appalling, disgusting, and disgraceful exhibition of football possibly in the history of the game . . . after seeing the film tonight, you at home may well think that teams that play in this manner ought to be expelled immediately from the competition.

The 1962 World Cup was held in Chile and the match that David Coleman was describing above was the home country's engagement with Italy. Unlike the giants of Argentina and Brazil, Chile's world reputation does not rest on its footballing prowess. Geographical extremes, turbulent politics, a great wine industry – but not football. And yet Chile has a complex and highly entertaining relationship with the World Cup ranging from the 'Battle of Santiago' in 1962 to one of the most extraordinary attempts ever to cheat their way into the finals.

The 1962 World Cup was held two years before I was born. My parents had discussed emigrating to Chile and even enquired at the Chilean embassy about the possibility. It was one of those plans that never came off and yet as a child I was taken over by one of those strange obsessions which people sometimes develop about another country and it has stayed with me ever since. I wanted to know everything, right down to street names and bus routes. Even now, after several visits, including a year living in Santiago, the moment of looking down from the plane window onto the weird and desolate Andes mountain range fills me with the same excitement as it did when I first arrived over ten years ago.

Back in 1962, Chile and Italy took to the pitch of the National

Stadium with bad feeling already present. According to Leonel Sanchez, Chile's star striker, the Italian press had been filing derogatory reports which appeared to revolve around the inferior charms of Chilean women. The insult to the nation's women was felt deeply by the Chilean players who were determined to avenge their honour. 'Many of us were married,' Sanchez remarked later as if the Italian insults were aimed directly at their wives. Aware of the bad vibe, the Italian players attempted a placatory gesture by carrying carnations onto the pitch, but the Chilean fans were in unforgiving mood. The flowers were rejected and the players were met by deafening boos and whistles. The stage was set for the 'Battle of Santiago'.

Five minutes into the game, a brawl broke out in which two Chilean players lay prone on the pitch, another Chilean was kicked nowhere near the ball and the Italian culprit was sent off. 'And now the army are on the pitch,' cried the commentator as the Italian player appeared reluctant to leave and about twenty uniformed men strode on to encourage him to accept his red card with good grace.

It was not, in fact, the army marching onto the pitch but the good old Chilean *carabineros*, a kind of militarised police force whose green uniforms became depressingly familiar during the 1980s as they intervened to break up protests against the Pinochet regime. The Chilean police have a reputation for incorruptibility almost unique in Latin America – there is no point in enquiring about 'on-the-spot-fines' if you are caught in any misdemeanour. They are also more than a match for any Italian defender in the thuggish stakes. In early 1988, during my first visit to Chile, I took part in a protest in which the participants were demanding to know the whereabouts of seven young men who had disappeared. The police arrived and began beating anybody they could lay their hands on. When I foolishly took what I thought was a sneaky photo of this, I found myself bundled into a van and heading for the local *comiseria*. Although I escaped relatively lightly in terms of physical mistreatment, I was able to witness at first hand what happened to one protester who had punched a policeman while being arrested.

Even when I returned in 1992, after the supposed end of military rule, the *pacos* (as the police are unaffectionately nicknamed) were lobbing tear gas into a peaceful march which had entered a crowded street. The horror of being trapped by this burning, stinging, choking gas produced a stampede in which escape became the only priority and the surrounding humanity simply an obstacle to this imperative of survival. We tore and scrabbled our way free while overhead a helicopter buzzed, calmly directing the forces on the ground.

Fortunately for the Italians in 1962, the police did not have quite such a free rein and under gentle persuasion from the Chilean 'forces of order' the Italian player left the pitch allowing the game to resume. But Leonel Sanchez had obviously taken the affront to Chilean womanhood more seriously than the other players, because when David hacked at his legs, he responded with a devastating left-hook that knocked the Italian out. For some reason, Sanchez was allowed to stay on the pitch and this was perhaps a little unfortunate for him because shortly afterwards, David responded with Cantona-like aplomb, delivering a flying kung-fu kick to the neck. David did leave the field, bringing the Italians down to nine men, but the aggression did not diminish. Rugby-tackles and raised fists continued throughout a game which Chile finally won 2-0. The finest moment in the game occurred after the final whistle when a Chilean went to shake an Italian's hand. The Italian *did* shake his hand but then punched him in the face as well. Perhaps the Chilean had also said something uncomplimentary about his mother – the basis for most Chilean insults.

Chile went on to come third in the competition by beating Yugoslavia, while Leonel Sanchez scored four goals to become joint highest scorer. Curiously, Sanchez attracted the attentions of Milan during the World Cup. Milan made a successful bid for him and soon the diminutive Chilean striker was heading for

Italy. Another player with the Milan squad at the time was David – Sanchez's adversary in the National Stadium. The players – in the finest tradition of the game – agreed it had all been a silly squall, became best mates, and David sportingly accepted the role of Cicerone to Sanchez in Milan. It is not known whether the tour of Milan's sights included checking out Italian women or jocular arguments as to how they compared with Santiago's finest.

Leonel Sanchez began his football with Universidad de Chile (as did Marcelo Salas, the player Alex Ferguson was sniffing around towards the end of 1997). Chilean clubs are weighed down by the history and development of the country – even the names bear the imprint of the past. In the port of Valparaiso, for example, the principal team is Wanderers – reflecting British mercantile penetration in the 19th Century. Just down the road in Vina del Mar there is Everton, a team almost as hopeless as their British counterparts. The waves of immigration into the country also gave rise to teams such as Audax Italiano, Palestino, and Union Espanola – all now in some decline. In the copper-producing north of the country, Cobreloa play in orange and retain close links to the copper industry. Chile's two most famous universities – Universidad Catolica and Universidad de Chile both produced teams which continue to bear their names. And Colo Colo, the 'team of the people', take their name from a legendary fleet-footed chieftain from Chile's Mapuche Indians. The Mapuches were the only indigenous people to halt the advance of the Spanish *conquistadores*, engaging in early guerrilla warfare which prevented the Spanish from penetrating below the Bio-Bio river in the south.

In the post-war period, one of the most eagerly awaited footballing contests was the *clasico universitario* between the two university teams. An evening game at the National Stadium would also be accompanied by spectacle and show, including dramatic interpretations of political and historical events by students from the two universities. The universities represent two very different traditions. The Universidad Catolica has always been the elite university with close links to the church hierarchy and with its stadium situated in the upper-class area of the city. The Universidad de Chile with a more radical lay tradition was the route for many students of lower-middle-class roots to gain access to higher education and was consequently less of a bastion of the establishment than the Catolica.

Currently, the fanatical supporters of 'La U' (as the Universidad de Chile is more commonly known) go under the name Los de Abajo (those at the bottom) but their rivalry is now far more intense with Colo Colo than with Universidad Catolica. Colo Colo is the 'popular' team in Chile, while the Catolica has few roots in the more marginal areas of the city where support for football is at its most fervent. Colo Colo and Universidad de Chile fans do battle with each other with an enthusiasm which matches the most bitter of enmities between British clubs. One of their favourite habits is to smash up each other's stadium, dancing gleefully on the ruins.

The nocturnal *clasico universitario*, with its mixture of football and erudite, popular theatre belongs to a tradition of both football and society which came under vicious assault following the 1973 military coup that overthrew the left-wing coalition of Salvador Allende. This was perhaps most potently symbolised by the National Stadium itself, which was quickly converted into a makeshift concentration camp. Photos of the time show working-class faces on the terraces, faces which belonged to people who had probably stood there on other occasions watching a match, perhaps even the infamous Chile vs Italy from eleven years before.

Many who were processed and tortured in the National Stadium survived to recount what happened to them. There are the nightmarish stories about the hooded figure who would walk the terraces pointing out former comrades to the accompanying soldiers. But there are also stories of humanity – the most interesting of which concerns a Swedish diplomat, some Uruguayans and the second-in-command of the stadium.

Following the coup in Chile, other Latin Americans became an instant target for repression since most of them were political exiles. The military junta rounded up Uruguayans, Brazilians, Bolivians and Argentinians and herded them to the National Stadium where many were slated for execution. Around fifty Uruguayans – most with connections to the Tupamaro urban guerrilla movement – were held in the stadium and it was known that execution was their most likely fate. At this point a Swedish diplomat called Harald Edelstam gained access to the stadium and made it his mission to save as many lives as possible. A shrewd judge of character, Edelstam noticed that Major Lavandero, who was an army career officer and second-in-command of the stadium, appeared to be disenchanted with his work. Knowing that the Uruguayans were due to die, Edelstam approached Lavandero. Edelstam told him that it was obvious he was no torturer and that he would personally ensure that the Uruguayans would leave Chile for Sweden if Lavandero would sign the release papers. Eventually Lavandero agreed and the Uruguayans were released. But when Edelstam returned to the stadium, hoping to persuade Lavandero to do the same for a group of Brazilians, he was met by the furious officer in charge of the stadium. Not only had the Brazilians already been executed but so had Major Lavandero for releasing the Uruguayans.

One year after the coup, when the stadium had been emptied of its prisoners, Chile qualified for the World Cup Finals. They did so, in part, because of the reputation acquired by the National Stadium. The Soviet Union honourably refused to play a qualifying match in the stadium, so soon after so much blood had been spilled there. Consequently, the Chilean team took to the field and scored several goals into an empty net, thus gaining their dubious passage to the World Cup at the expense of the Soviets.

The Soviet refusal to play in the National Stadium was mirrored for some time by an unwillingness on the part of the population to attend sporting events there. The *clasico universitario* did not fare well under military rule, which could not tolerate the mixture of satire and political comment which the theatrical spectacle provided, while the harsh effects of neo-liberal economic restructuring also meant that fewer low-income families could attend football matches.

Despite the terrible events which took place in the National Stadium, it has remained a focal point for football in Chile and has been reintegrated into Chilean cultural and sporting life. The stadium has become part of normality again and, while nobody forgets what happened there, it is still possible to sit on a spring evening as the setting sun dazzles the snow on the surrounding mountain peaks, watching the players below and thinking only about such weighty matters as how a really penetrating long ball wouldn't go amiss every now and again.

I think that there are various reasons for this. First, the National Stadium was not designed as a concentration camp, but it was briefly appropriated by the military for that purpose as were other important public spaces across the country. Many other historic and sporting events took place in the stadium, including the 1962 World Cup, Allende's inaugural speech, and countless *clasicos universitarios*. The stadium has been reclaimed not just as part of Chile's history but also as a stadium. It was the military who violently disrupted its tradition and, although the process has taken time, reclaiming the stadium in its ordinariness, rather than as a demonised 'house of horrors' is a powerful rebuff to the military's attempt to terrorise the population.

Part of this reclaiming process took place in the mid-1980s when the Pope visited Chile. He blessed the stadium and acknowledged what had happened there, something which many Chileans saw as symbolically important. During his speech in the stadium to Chilean youth, the Pope also called upon them to reject a variety of sins. With a rhetorical flourish, he tossed questions to the massed youth inviting them to roar their rejection of the sin in question which they dutifully did. When, however, he demanded to know if they would resist carnal temptation, there was a moment of superb silence and then a crescendoing NO rippled around the terraces. The Pope appeared visibly disconcerted by this healthy honesty among his young flock.

As the Pinochet regime grew less secure, the stadium also became the focus for political opposition during military rule; it was one of the few places where collective vocal opposition could be expressed. 'The dictatorship is going to fall' was commonly heard chanted on the terraces. Even today, the young fanatics of *Los de Abajo*, hanging from the perimeter fence of the stadium, taunt the police about their role supporting Pinochet during the dictatorship, the police often genially responding by allowing their dogs to run free into the crowd. The Chilean Armed Forces – of which the police are officially a part – manifested a total contempt for civil society during their years in power. This hostility was particularly strong towards young people and became almost pathological towards what was perceived as the loutish anarchistic rabble of young football supporters.

The degeneration of football under military rule saw the decline and demise of many traditional clubs. The generals also attempted to control football directly, with Pinochet declared Honorary President of Colo Colo. Some justice was later restored when Pinochet received a massive rebuff from Carlos Caszely – one of Colo Colo and Chile's most famous players. During the 1988 plebiscite, in which voters were asked to say yes or no to Pinochet remaining in power, the opposition produced an advert in which a frail old woman recounts her imprisonment and torture under the junta. Just as this begins to appear like any other testimony, Caszely walks onto the bare set, puts his arm around the woman and says that he knows that she is telling the truth. He knows this because the silver-haired old lady is his mum. The advert caused a sensation in Chile and helped defeat Pinochet in the plebiscite. Caszely was a kind of Lineker figure in Chilean football and the advert certainly puts the latter's Walker's crisps efforts into perspective.

Nowhere, however, was the corruption of standards under

military rule more dramatically manifested than in Chile's extraordinary attempt to cheat its way into Italia '90.

In the qualifiers for Italia '90, Chile had to play and beat Brazil by two goals in the Maracaña stadium. During the game, which Chile were losing 1-0, the goalkeeper 'Condor' Rojas (so-called for his extremely large beaky nose) fell to the ground claiming to have been injured by a firework thrown by an opposing supporter. Fernando Astengo, Chile's captain, promptly led his team from the pitch in protest, hoping that the game would either be replayed or Chile awarded the victory. Photographic evidence showed, however, that the firework had landed some feet from Rojas and that his injuries were self-inflicted. As a result, the promising Astengo was banned from football for four years, Rojas was banned for life (he became a born-again Christian), while Chile were banned from the World Cup until 1998.

Chile's exclusion from the World Cup was felt keenly. It was humiliating for a country which still prided itself on its low levels of corruption and traditions of integrity in public life. In many ways, the incident in the Maracaña was symbolic of the degeneration which had taken place under military rule. It was as if the spiv get-rich-quick mentality of the Chicago Boys, and the impunity with which an ex-Minister could be blown up by the Secret Police on the streets of Washington DC, had combined to produce the climate in which such an extraordinary attempt to cheat could even be contemplated. Chilean pride was also dented by the sheer silliness of it, especially when those who believed the initial version of events had gone to protest outside the Brazilian embassy. When Brazilian photographers produced images of a firework landing some distance from the goalkeeper and *then* the goalie collapsing in supposed agony, the humiliation was almost too much to bear.

Exclusion from the World Cup also affected a generation of players who did not get the chance to take part in international competition. Players such as Ivan Zamorano (ex Real Madrid and now with Inter Milan) and Ivo Basay were deprived of their chance to play at the top international level. One of the beneficial aspects, however, of the ban on Chilean football was a growing obsession with the youth team. In the absence of World Cup football, attention shifted to the talented youngsters coming through the Under 17 national selection. Rangers fans have had the chance to see one of these players, although some die-hards must have been alarmed to know they were about to sign another player from a Papist country who had also played for a team called Universidad Catolica. They would doubtless have been relieved to find that Sebastian Rozental, as his name suggests, is Jewish. Their appreciation of him has been brief, however, because he promptly succumbed to a long-term injury.

In November 1997, Chile played once again in the National Stadium, needing to beat Bolivia to qualify for France 1998. They managed to do so without resorting to fireworks and will be taking their place with the other Latin American nations. The Chilean fans have managed to retain the honourable tradition of rioting to celebrate their victories and doing battle with the boys in green. Mass arrests have accompanied Chile's World Cup qualifier victories as youth ran amok in the centre of Santiago and the police abandoned their fragile modicum of restraint to engage in their favourite pastime of beating up their own citizens.

It is hard to say how Chile will do in France. Certainly, they can be considered the weakest of the Latin American teams. Ironically, they have been drawn in the same group as Italy and it will be interesting to see whether the shadow of 1962 still falls over this game, whether any pre-match dissing of Italian or Chilean women heralds atrocities on the pitch. The Chileans bring with them some talented players and an eccentric World Cup history – from the 'Battle of Santiago' against the Italians, to their qualifying match against a Soviet ghost team in a stadium of ghosts, and the ludicrous events in Brazil where 'Condor' Rojas suffered his legendary non-assault with a firework.

Chile is a place of extremes, which is perhaps not so surprising in a country which stretches from the rainless Atacama desert down to freezing Antarctica. Indeed, the colonising Spanish referred to Santiago *del nuevo extremo* – the new extremity of a flat world. Physically isolated by the Andes mountain range, it has also been cut off from world football for a long time. But as the team runs out in France, and the lone-star tricolours flutter on the terraces, I will at least have no doubt as to my second team in the championship.

Let Your Feelings Slip

Christopher Kenworthy

At school, I was known as the Spastic. You might think that's offensive to spastics, but imagine how I felt. The nickname arose because I was convinced that footballs were designed merely to slap legs and noses, or to splash mud over me. I spent every game hiding behind other players; my lack of co-ordination, and angular bursts away from the ball made me look a bit peculiar. When everybody else was charging upfield, I was trying to show the teacher that something was wrong with my hands. The cold had turned them orange, the same colour as breadcrumbs on ham. His advice? Rub them together. At the time I thought he was being vindictive. I was pretty soft, I suppose.

This is the sort of story that you tell to your girlfriend, thinking she'll find it endearing, but it just makes her look at you as though to say, *I didn't know* that *about you*. Or at least that's the way it was with Julia Walker. I'd tell her stories to make her laugh, and would then spend twice as long retracting them. She'd usually end those conversations with a speculation such as, 'I wonder what sort of a father you'd make then.' I didn't find her attitude very helpful.

The truth is, things hurt me. I tried to hide it, but I was constantly aching. The slightest cut for me was agony. On a cold day, the earache spread right through my head. The briefest sunshine gave me sunburn. But living in Preston, that wasn't much of a problem. More than physical pain, though, I was susceptible to loss. If something went wrong in my life, I didn't just cry and cheer up like most people. My gums would start to flake, my arse would bleed. Sensitive is how I would have put it. My Dad just thought I was soft. He may have had a point.

Julia didn't have any time for my pain. She was intelligent, and she retained facts well enough to brighten up any conversation. She was also perceptive, so that no matter how I tried to jolly an afternoon along, she'd see through my guise. Saying I was fine only caused her eyebrows to slide up her forehead. Whenever I admitted that something was bothering me, she'd accuse me of wallowing. 'How much pain are you in on any given day?' she asked once.

The real problem wasn't even obvious to her. More than anything, I was hurt by happiness. If something went well, I felt pain. If somebody showed friendship or love, it made me want to cry. If I saw people celebrating, being really happy, all I wanted to do was bawl. Seeing my Dad's face after one of England's best goals in '86 hurt so much I had to leave the room.

This inability to deal with happiness probably went on all through my childhood, but I think it began during a Wednesday afternoon football match. I had been doing a rain dance during break, in an attempt to get the game cancelled. It had worked before, so I persisted. All I managed to whip up was an icy wind, and the match went ahead. Ten minutes later the ball was accidentally lobbed in front of me. I managed to kick it and run, kick and run; I was running up the field controlling the ball, hearing everybody behind me, heading towards a nervous goalie who loped from side to side. I missed, of course, but I'm not even sure by how much, because I was already focusing on my pain. It had felt so good to be in control, to be the one everybody was cheering for, that I was overwhelmed with sadness. Everybody saw the tears in my eyes, and assumed it was because I'd missed.

'Spastic,' Ian Jackson said flatly, before tippy-toeing off to get the ball and score his next goal.

An emotional hypochondriac, Julia called me, and my doctor was even less sympathetic. He was a handsome Indian, who sat incredibly still without ever moving his head, no matter how angry he became.

'It's not my problem. What can I do? Sort yourself out, Stephen. Get a grip. You've so much to be happy about, why do you complain? There are plenty of people worse off than you.'

'But I'm still unhappy.'

'You're just a drifter, Stephen. This girl you're with; you don't love her. Get a wife. Settle down.'

A glaring cultural difference was revealed by that conversation, but he was right about one thing. I was staying with Julia for every wrong reason that existed. The main one being that it was easier than being alone.

After that conversation, however, something changed. By accepting that my relationship with Julia was doomed, I was able to relax, side-stepping her criticisms and sneers, so that we had a good time. We went to a park, and it didn't rain. We drank red wine, had a small picnic. Cuddled in public. It was so good that by the time she was kissing my ear and nuzzling into my neck, I felt sad. I was shocked out of it when I saw an aura around her, the colour of gas flame, but steady. She saw that I was staring and the glow withdrew.

'What did you see?'

'Just the look on your face,' I lied.

She went quiet for the next hour. Apparently I'm not the only one who feels bad when things are going well. Whatever had beamed out of Julia that night must have disturbed her. It was some time since I'd seen the glow, but I knew it was brought on by intensity. Strong feelings warm people with light.

It happened again during the World Cup. Summer of '98. I'd split up with Julia shortly after that time in the park, and met Lauren Bolton at a party. It was one of those occasions when I was standing back from the crowd because I genuinely wanted some time to myself, but my caution intrigued her and she came to talk to me. I remember being sick on my knees at one point and she wiped me up. Later we were kissing, and although I could still taste vomit, she didn't seem to mind.

Lauren came from Blackburn, but was a determined Accrington

fan. Her strong accent made her sound as thick as the rest of us, but she was remarkably happy for somebody from East Lancs. Intelligent, as well. She must have been pretty lonely out there. 'I love football,' she said, and I could tell she thought I'd be impressed. Rather than show her I was the one male in ten thousand that didn't bother with the game, I said it was a relief to know we could share that.

We slept with each other on the first night, but she was clever enough for that not to matter. After we made love I got a spasm down my back, the muscles bunching up. I over-reacted a bit, then tried to play it down. Julia used to get mad at me when that happened, so I didn't want to bother Lauren with it. But she wanted to know what was wrong. When I explained she said, 'Oh, poor lamb.' That was an unusual intimacy from somebody on a first night. I wondered if she talked to all men like that. To look at she was plain enough, but her face always had a sleepy smile. As we lay there, the curtains open to let in moonlight, she said, 'I won't sleep tonight. I want to watch you.' With some women that would be terrifying. You'd be looking for the gash marks in their arms. With Lauren, I trusted that it was pure joy at being with me, and let myself sleep while she gazed.

A few days later, we agreed to watch the World Cup together. 'If you'd rather watch with your mates,' she kept saying, leaving the sentence hanging, but I assured her I'd rather watch with her. I remembered some of the rules from school, and soon picked up enthusiasm. I even went to the library and read some books. There were systems and plans, intricate waves of interaction flowing down the pitch. I was impressed. I'd always thought footballers were mindless, but that's because I listened to the interviews. Lauren taught me not to bother. Forget *Football Focus*, dismiss the après-match dissection; just watch the game. She had a point. If you never hear them open their mouths, they look deep and beautiful. Even Gazza.

Sharing her bean bag, drinking neat vodka (her choice), we watched most of the World Cup. Every time England won or drew, she was subsequently more intense in bed. A real enthusiast, she chanted the word 'more' just enough to make it exciting, without ever being too demanding of me.

She wasn't the only person to use football as a way to hold my interest. When I was about seven, just before he first went into hospital, my Dad tried the same thing. If nothing else, we must be able to talk about football. He assumed. It was the one way he tried to communicate with me, and the one way he couldn't. At the time I was into poetry and country lanes. I liked blossom and streams.

While I was seeing Lauren, Dad ended up in hospital again. It had been a regular occurrence over the past fifteen years, but one that always made me nervous and bad tempered. He wasn't a man who smiled much, so to see his face light up wherever I went in to visit made me wince.

One night, after I'd been to see him, I needed a distraction. The drive back from the Lancaster hospital was just on the wrong side of long, and I was anxious. He'd been worse than ever, the colour going out of his skin, so that his ginger beard looked stark and greasy. While I'd been sitting with him it went over and over in my mind how much his beard looked like genital hair. This was still on my mind when I got home, but Lauren rang up within five minutes, and I invited her round. We spent the night in bed. For the first time, she said that she loved me. The room was dark, but around her fingers, which rested on her breasts, there was a blue light. As she moved her hand to her face the light spread, like a silk scarf around her face.

I started crying, and was unable to prevent myself from hacking loudly into the pillow. I expected her to question me and demand to know what was wrong, but she put her arms around me, and said I'd be all right.

'It's just because of your Dad,' she whispered.

'It's not,' I said. 'It feels more like happiness. Because I'm with you.'

It reminded me of a time when I was young, on holiday in the

Isle of White. It was a fantastic afternoon, down at the Old Park beach, surfing on a polystyrene board, making sand troughs and castles. Dad was sitting on a rock, and he grabbed me as I ran past, put me on his knee and bounced me up and down. I felt so happy that I cried. I couldn't stop myself. He looked horrified. I couldn't show him my feelings, couldn't say, 'Dad I'm happy because you're with me,' so when he asked what was wrong I said that the bouncing hurt. 'Why?' he demanded, furious, as though I was accusing him. So I said my brother had kicked me in the balls earlier that day. It didn't go down at all well, with Dad throwing me onto the sand, and storming off. He never touched me again after that.

The strange thing was that as I watched him walk away, his body was rimmed with blue light. It was the same colour as the glow you see around a stadium at night. I don't know if it was the remnant of his happiness, or his newfound fury, but there was no doubt he'd been moved.

At that point, I hadn't seen the blue glow since Ian Jackson's funeral. Children were never allowed to adult funerals, but when one of our own died, most of the class was taken along. The blue glow was over the congregation, much as you'd expect, burning brightly as the narrow coffin was lowered into the ground. The strangest thing, for me, was that the graveyard backed onto the school field. It was one of those graveyards that's just a lawn with holes in it, rather than the trees, mist and tombs you imagine. Schools are meant to be enclosed places, but our football field was separated from the graveyard by nothing more than a grassy ditch. You'd think kids would be freaked out by that, but we took it for granted. We always called it the Church End, rather than the Graveyard. At Jackson's funeral, I noticed that if I closed one eye, to flatten the perspective, the gravestones at the farthest edge looked exactly the same shape and size as the gym wall. Which is more significant than you might think, because that's where I'd killed him.

It was an accident of course, and it came shortly after his first show of interest in me. These days, school crazes revolve around the latest toy, game cartridge, or drug. In the seventies we were on a more spiritual plane. And I'm not just talking about conkers and marbles, because we tried some pretty weird stuff. Ouija boards, lifting people by finger tips so they levitated out of our hands, hypnotism, even a touch of black magic. But the weirdest craze was heart stopping. Literally.

I don't remember who I learnt it from, or why I became the expert, but I was soon known for stopping hearts. At the lunch break, I'd assemble a crowd by the gym wall to watch me perform, before initiating others into the faint. My assistant was Simon Christian, who dutifully performed the ritual. I crouched down, took five deep breaths, holding the last one in, stood up quickly, and then leaned against the wall while Simon pressed on my heart, as though giving CPR. Within seconds, I would faint.

Each time it happened, the first thing I noticed was a blue trimming of light over the Pedders Lane housing estate to the left of the church. Then the faces of those watching me as the view darkened, and I sensed the ground coming towards me. I'd come round quickly, still deaf for a few seconds as my brain slurred back into action.

Don't try this at home, kids. I'm not pissing about here. It works, and it's dangerous.

I assumed the blue glow was an artefact of fainting. Now I know it's something you can see when people are enflamed by passion. The faint simply opened me up to it.

At the time, I was more interested in the way this new activity brought attention to me. Forced fainting appealed to everybody, even Jackson. Especially when he realised that the ritual removed pain. We found that out because Jackson was worried. He wanted a go, but he said watching me land heavily looked painful.

'I never feel a thing, ' I told him.

He made me prove it, by getting me to go through the faint, and just as the blue glow appeared behind him and around him, he punched me in the face. I was aware of it, but felt nothing, and slumped passively to the floor.

After that he was proud of me. Ian Jackson was going to be my friend. I noticed the irony. By quivering on the floor and drooling, I had discarded the label of Spastic. I was accepted.

In return for his grinny show of friendship, I gave Ian Jackson the faint. He knelt before me, taking his breaths dutifully, standing up, staring into my eyes as I pressed his chest. I felt his heart pump against my hand, and stop, the ebb of it running up my arm, the way the swing of a pendulum passes through your bones when you grab it.

The look on his face, the shock, should have given it away. He slumped down, looking asleep, rather than knocked out. After that, I can remember the panic, seeing him in the foetal position, teachers running up. Spontaneously, those who were present constructed a myth of how Jacko simply fainted while we were playing football. The teachers weren't interested in explanations and picked his blue body up, running away with him.

Shortly after that night with Lauren, when I cried for no obvious reason, I went to visit Dad again. Most of the time was spent in awkward pauses between his descriptions of hospital rituals and the surface details of my recent life. He said something strange at one point. Discounting his illness, assuming he wouldn't die, he said, 'I need a purpose in life. And football just isn't it.'

I was amazed he could even consider it. I never knew it mattered to him that much. There'd been this vague intention to be a football coach, to start an amateur club. He must have been referring to that.

Before I left, his bed was lined up with the others to watch the World Cup final. I was meant to be spending the afternoon with Lauren, but my Dad had kept me talking. Just before I left he'd said something, about Shearer's knee, a concerned look on his face. Then he said, 'You're a whiny little twat.'

'I know.'

'Just cheer up.'

I walked out just as the starting whistle was blown.

Driving back, I put the radio on. It's more exiting than watching it on TV. There's a shared camaraderie on the road; a minority of drivers are out there because they hate football, but those with their heads angled towards the centre of the car are listening for goals. At traffic lights, we were all looking at each other, nodding approval. Once I was out of Lancaster, heading south on the A6, I passed through an area where radio reception was less then reliable. The hills around Garstang, coupled with masses of electricity pylons, made static the channel of choice. During the ten-minute journey to Lauren's flat I picked out several cheers, and a few disparate phrases: 'He's through, he's through . . . shot on . . . running up . . . a nice bit off . . . like Titan's spear . . . a truly superlative attempt . . .'

It wasn't at all clear how we were doing. The final decay into static occurred about a mile from my destination.

The point is, my Dad was right. There's no need to be so miserable. You don't have to be so bloody soft. There's nothing endearing about it. If you sulk off into a corner trying to look deep and introspective, people just think you're a cunt. People will love you if you spend time with them, and stop being so aloof. I might have dismissed his comments, except that as I drove back into Preston, there was a blue glow over the Pedders Lane Estate, spreading out over the tower blocks, down towards the docks. It doesn't matter that it's a game, that it's a ball and a net and a bunch of grunts. People choose to care, and that's enough for me.

I parked badly, and ran up to the flat. I let myself in and Lauren smiled. She wasn't mad at me for being late, just glad that I'd arrived safely. Her eyes looked bluer than usual, as though some

of the light was seeping out of them. She motioned towards the
TV, trying to get me to see the score. More than anything, her
face showed that she was pleased to see me. How can you argue
with that?

Cheese Crackers

Pete Davies

It's the cheese women I remember. You'd think it'd be Platt's lightning swivel-and-volley in the 119th minute in Bologna, the instinctive brilliance of Cameroon's attacking play in Naples, or the raw and brutal recklessness of their defenders when they threw that quarter-final away. You'd think, of course, that it'd be the penalties in Turin, and Gascoigne's tears – and for sure, I can hit the mental pause button and those images remain fresh, still vivid eight years on. They're totem moments, packed with colour and noise from one joyful, draining summer month that held England in thrall, and which I was privileged to enjoy from a ringside seat. But all the same, if you mention Italia '90 to me now, the first thing that springs to mind is the cheese women.

Perhaps I've mythologised them; perhaps they've taken on a private significance bulking unnaturally large in my mind. But I do know I've not invented them; they really were there, those amazons dressed in uniforms of retina-searing buttercup yellow. In the media centres, the Italian World Cup staff came in a variety of colour-coded outfits – blue, green, red for the Coca Cola people, the men in blazers and the women in sharp suits – but even amid this sartorial Jackson Pollock, the blazing yellow of the cheese women did brightly stand out.

In an environment everywhere bedecked with corporate free-bies and puffery, a whole universe of logos and slogans, the cheese women were a minor marketing triumph. Japanese multi-nationals and American fizzy pop may have pumped in the big money, but somewhere down the many rungs of the sponsorship ladder, the makers and promoters of Grana Padano – the cheese in question – pulled off the PR trick that matters. Eight years on, their brand recognition remains immediate in my mind. You say to me Italia '90, and what do I say to you? I say, cheese women, I say Grana Padano.

It wasn't just the yellow, mind. I accept that in the mounting madness attendant upon following a World Cup, I may in the later stages have been prone to all manner of hallucination – but unless I'm very much mistaken, the cheese women got *taller*. They stood out in the flustered and hustling throngs not only by virtue of their garish garb, but also because by the end they were giantesses, Latin sex titans looming over the hacks like fragrant cloned Venuses in a crowd of sweaty midgets. Had Grana Padano employed a squad of basketball players? And what on earth did it have to do with football?

Nothing, of course. But marketing, sponsorship, mega-corporate razzle-dazzle – it's the financial oil that lubricates all big sport in the modern world, and pretty much everything else too. Take politics – it has, these days, succumbed almost entirely to the wiles of the PR people, fallen from ideas and policies to sound bites and spin. New Labour in the '97 election was as much a promotional as a political spectacle, and big business ran alongside it with its tongue hanging out all the way.

Indeed, knowing the current marketing potency of football, Labour frequently couched their victoriously vacuous campaign in the language of the game. Blair climaxed his speech to conference in 1996 with a riff from Skinner & Baddiel, 'Labour's coming home'. Another of the politicans – now a junior minister of something or other – said to me of their campaign, two weeks before the vote, 'We've won the away leg 2–0. All we've got to do now is keep the ball.'

In that campaign New Labour, you could argue, were to politics what Sky has been to football. Never mind the substance, just check out the camera angles – and to grumble about this invasion of every sphere of our life by the salesmen is, it seems, to take issue with a force as unstoppable as the tide rushing in on Canute. As it applies to both politics and football, however, the effect is to reduce what ought to be important (politics) or merely enjoyable (football) to a kind of hysterical blandness, a monotonous, ersatz gibberish of empty hype, a tabloid froth in which footballers or politicans become indistinguishable from pop stars and soap actors. The bigger and noisier it gets, in other words (and what could be bigger than a 32-nation World Cup?) the less it means, and the less I care.

Shock! Heresy! Football writer doesn't care about football! Not true, of course. I watch all the televised football I can throughout every season; evenings with my son in front of midweek European games are a particular favourite. As for the real thing, when time and work allow we'll watch matches at the Alfred MacAlpine in Huddersfield – the Alf, as the fanzines dubbed it – or at Armthorpe Welfare on a Sunday, when the Doncaster Belles are at home. So don't get me wrong, I like my football all right – but whatever I may have thought or written when I was younger, it's not blood and life.

I make no great claim (as seems obligatory among the New Laddage these days) to have supported any particular club since I was in the womb. The sperm that won the race and hit an egg to make me wasn't travelling in an over-priced away shirt. I just watch my local club when I can, because that's what I think a person should do – a belief that very likely means I may soon give up even on Huddersfield, and start spending my Saturdays in the Unibond League. As for watching the Belles, you'll have to read my book about it if you want that one explaining. But either way and overall, from non-league to Old Trafford, I don't believe that football really matters very much. Certainly, it doesn't matter as much as its now ubiquitously dominant position in the culture would seem to suggest. Nor do I think this bloated monster of a 32-nation World Cup matters either, not really. I'll watch it, I'll enjoy it – but it doesn't *matter*.

At the risk of stating the grindingly obvious, here's a list of a few things that do matter. Poverty. Homelessness. Crime. Underfunded health and education systems. Global warming. But

Keegan resigns at Newcastle, or Cantona hangs up his boots, and it's Hold The Front Page, isn't it? I'm pressed to the conclusion that we live in a climate of galloping frivolity – and that there's no bigger circus turn to distract us from what matters than football.

A few years ago, Maggie Brown in the *Independent* described the game as 'A form of male soap opera, a window on a strange world where drama, dirt, deals and a certain type of brilliant but limited physical talent mix and swirl around.' Well, maybe – but it's become a soap of cosmic proportion, bawling and spouting all the way from front page to back by way of the business pages in between. The spectacle of crazed European moguls buying teenagers for £20,000,000, of Newcastle's share price plunging when Shearer gets injured, of footballers earning more in a week than most people see in a year (or two, or three) – it's bigger than *Coronation Street*, isn't it?

Even within sport, football outfaces every other game in town. More people go to one game at Old Trafford than attend all six games in a weekend's programme of top league rugby union put together. Manchester United's turnover is bigger than the whole of rugby league. Last summer I was at a one-day game between the women's cricket teams of England and South Africa – and OK, you'd not expect overwhelming media attention for a game of women's cricket. But present at that game was one of the English Cricket Board's senior coaches, and he complained with some bitterness that football was squeezing out men's cricket, never mind the women.

So I could do with us getting a sense of perspective. (I also look forward to seeing pigs fly, dressed in tutus and brandishing inflatable bananas.) But really, I look at this behemoth of a spectacle now looming in France, this orgy not just of sport but of economics and advertising, and of national myth-making too – and there's a little piece of me that wishes I could hop in a time machine, pop back to Uruguay in 1930, and find out what this World Cup thing was like when it began. Was football ever sensible? Did it ever know its place?

And what was the American team like? Unless you're a stat hound and a terminal junkie for quirk facts and trick questions, I'll lay money you didn't know the USA were semi-finalists in the first World Cup. They were mostly emigrant Brits, playing their football in the eastern seaboard's American Soccer League (it flourished briefly in the twenties, and went belly-up with the Depression; teams included the Brooklyn Wanderers, and the poetically fetching Providence Clamdiggers). So they went along, beat Belgium and Paraguay 3–0 apiece, met Argentina in the last four, and found themselves on the wrong end of a 6–1 tonking.

But really, what was it like? Was it a festival of gentlemanly good grace, unsullied by all the attendant palavers of the modern age? Erm . . . actually, when Uruguay beat Argentina 4–2 in the final, an enraged mob across the River Plate in Buenos Aires attacked the Uruguayan consulate, and was only dispersed when the police started shooting. Football, it seems, was always mad.

Right from the off, the World Cup's been marked by pets and intrigues variously childish and sinister. Uruguay, for example, didn't turn up in Italy for the second tournament in 1934 to defend their title. This was partly because they were piqued that only four European nations (France, Romania, Yugoslavia, and Belgium) bothered to get on the boat and go to their own bash four years earlier – and it was partly because of a players' strike. But maybe defending their title against a host nation led by Mussolini would have been too much to ask anyway. In the quarter-finals the Italians kicked so many lumps out of the Spanish that when it went to a replay, only four of the Spanish were fit to start the second game. But having Il Duce for your boss, I suppose, would add a special twist to the notion of the home side playing under pressure.

Besides, Italy were hardly unique in the lump-kicking department. Brazil had a grotesque punch-up with Czechoslovakia in 1938, and another with Hungary in 1954, this latter apparently extending to the use of broken bottles as weapons in the Hungarian changing room after the game. West Germany, meanwhile, could be argued to have won that '54 title by kicking Ferenc Puskas off the park in the opening match, just as Portugal kicking Pelé from pillar to post in '66 may well have helped Brazil lose their way in our own World Cup.

These are, of course, isolated incidents in the history of a tournament liberally marked by all manner of turbulent excitements, and the passionate intensity that sometimes spills over into studdings and fisticuffs will always be there. It's the point, isn't it? I just mention them to make my own point that when I say the game is out of hand now, it's not because I'm looking back to some golden age when all was sweet and clean – there never was such a time. The reason it's out of hand is instead because in the past two decades, something that was already fiercely emotional has had a bonfire of money lit beneath it, fuelling it into flames of mutant and gigantic dimension. In other words, football was always mad. The difference now is that it's mad and rich.

You'd have to make Argentina '78 the turning point – not so much a kickfest as a sickfest. The generals had taken over two years earlier; the World Cup was held in a nation where thousands were routinely being tortured, raped, and disappeared, and allowing that to happen can only be seen as an act of the most depressing cynicism. For Coca Cola to backstop the event financially to the tune of some $8,000,000, however, seems even more squalid. In Argentina, evidently, no one could hear you scream – least of all FIFA, their ears filled with the fizz and bubble of the corporate dollar.

These days, of course, FIFA has grown into a most lavish worldwide spectacle, in whose name hundreds of besuited grandees go junketeering round the first class flightpaths of Planet Football. There's a marvellous moment in Justin Cartwright's novel *Interior* when, having successfully pulled off a coup in a small West African nation, a member of the new government makes a public statement. The new regime, he announces, will immediately enter negotiations with the three most important world bodies – the UN, the World Bank, and FIFA. So it's strange to think now that in another world, many moons ago, all FIFA had was a private house in Zurich, staffed by a receptionist and a pair of snoozing dogs.

What happened? What happened was Jean Marie Faustin Godefroid Havelange – Joao for short. A Rio businessman, formerly an Olympic athlete (swimming in 1936, water polo in 1950), Havelange became President of the Brazilian Sports Association, and saw to it in 1970 that his country's wonder team had funds and facilities properly to prepare for the Mexico World Cup through three uninterrupted months. Then, with the Jules Rimet trophy on the shelf for good, and with glamour-laden Brazilian players travelling by his side, Havelange started racking up the air miles seeking election to the presidency of FIFA.

It was the first seriously globewide election campaign ever undertaken by a sports administrator, an epic gladhanding sortie in which he toured the smaller nations of the world bearing wondrous promises. Vote Joao, he told them, and they'd get a bigger World Cup, other competitions to play in, coaching and development facilities – in short, he promised that football really would be the world game.

Havelange was elected to run FIFA in 1974, and the missionary element in what took him to victory is all well and good – why, after all should Europe and South America have it all sewn up? (And roll on the day when an African side wins their first World Cup, too.) But obviously, someone had to fund his grand schemes for expansion – so when the first World Youth Cup for players under twenty was held in Tunisia in 1977, three years after Havelange's election, what was it called? It was called the FIFA Coca Cola Cup.

Seven years later, in 1984, I was in Morocco when Platini's French side won the European Championship. While I was there – in the little fishing port of Essaouira, if memory serves – I watched a game between two local sides on a pitch of red dirt, the fans in their djellabehs sitting in the broiling sun on temporary scaffold stands. And whose name was on the banners and pennants over the gate, and all along the stands? Again, Coca Cola.

What we'd arrived at was, in effect, the first globally conceived marketing campaign. Football, television, and Coke joined hands in a lucrative trinity; sponsorship was reborn as a perpetual motion machine, the Real Thing circling in four-year orbit round the football calendar. To give it the reach and the payback (and for the little countries to get what they voted for) the World Cup was enlarged come Spain '82 to twenty-four teams. By the time of Italia '90, the price at the door for companies wanting their exclusive tag on this PR honeypot was some $20,000,000 each. That's just the 'Official Partners', the likes of Mastercard, Coke, Gillette and JVC sitting at FIFA's top table. Then you've got the 'Marketing Partners' tied in to the local organisers of the tournament, and under them again you've got all the licensed outfits coughing up to stick the World Cup logo on their products.

In Italy, there were forty-seven of these licensees – so everywhere you went on World Cup territory you ate the official pasta, drank the official mineral water, sipped the official coffee, and snacked on the official Grana Padano as served up by giant beauties in yellow uniforms. So how many such sponsors, I wonder, will there be in France, when there are thirty-two teams, and enough football to fill the screens of the world with logos 'til your eyes pop? And how many tickets will all those companies get, in return for their handsome favours?

A year before the World Cup in the United States, I went to US Cup '93 in Boston, Washington, and Chicago. At Soldier Field, I watched the USA play Germany; they lost a surprisingly close game 4–3, and 53,000 were well entertained. But in my hotel the night before the game, I met a guy who had two company tickets, and he wasn't going to use them. When I told him that in a fan's eyes he was committing an abuse of privilege, he looked taken aback. He said, 'Well, I suppose I might go and see a half.' And there was something about his insouciance that could drive a bloke completely cheese crackers. With brand name cheese, of course.

Still, you get empty seats at Wimbledon too. At the golf and the motor racing, at the cricket and the rugby, hospitality tents and boxes swell with boneheads and bimbos not remotely interested in the sport at the centre of the event they're attending. It's just the way it is; we want a circus, and we need the sponsors to fund the marquee. If Havelange hadn't been there, someone else would have done it; football developing into this huge corporate creature has an historical inevitability about it. You can't stop it, any more than I'd wish for one minute to return the English game to the dreadful mire of the eighties, when the stadiums were urinals of rubble and litter, tragedy lurking in every shabby stand. But the rampant commercialisation of our sport does bring with it, all the same, a sense of loss.

The ordinary fan is less and less a participant, more and more a consumer – and one to be taken for ever higher ticket prices at that. In the process, the umbilical link between club and community has long been severed. As the likes of Brighton and Doncaster teeter along the rim of implosion and bankruptcy, the big clubs head rapidly towards a time when they'll wholly overshadow the landscape, spiritual partners to the franchise machines of American football. How am I to persuade my son that his local team is Huddersfield, when the marketing grasp of Man U has its teeth in him already? And how am I to be persuaded myself that the outcome of this World Cup is of any import whatsoever, when the tournament had become such a gargantuan vehicle for the promotion of its backers?

I'll watch it, sure. I don't doubt I'll enjoy it. But all the while I'll be wondering what the official cheese is, and whether the women who serve it are as tall as Grana Padano's amazons at Italia '90.

The Killing Fields

Jimmy Burns

To Maria-Laura

My name is Juan Aranda. I was born in Buenos Aires on 20th September 1955. I would like to tell you that my mother, like Maradona's, gave birth to me on a Sunday, a day for masses and football, screaming GOOOOAL, as she delivered me bloody and slimy into the world. But I came into this world in the midst of betrayal not hope, a fact that seems to have marked my destiny ever since.

For I was born the day Peron was overturned by a military coup led by right-wing generals and admirals. My mother, who had a picture of Evita next to her crucifix, began her contractions as Peron took refuge on a Paraguayan gunboat. She was giving birth as the radio in the hospital ward announced that the Junta had accepted Peron's resignation. So the doctors told my poor father later, it was the phrase *Hijos de Puta* – sons of bitches – that she uttered half deliriously as her womanhood split and her first-born son came tumbling out. It was unclear – and has remained so ever since – whether she was referring to the Junta, the Perons, or my father and me. That Sunday there was no football, only the sound of tanks rumbling through the streets of the city. It was in fact a bad year for football all round. Boca lost, for the third consecutive year, the championship to River.

Memory is in the eye of the beholder. You can make it dark as night or sweet as honey although time has a habit of getting ahead of one. Time sifts. Time heals. The pain of loss is absorbed into the compromise of being. And yet how easily do certain dates and places touch the hidden recesses of the heart, how unexpected the emotional charge of circumstance.

I am writing this from Paris, a city to which I have returned after a twenty-year absence. I am here not out of choice but out of necessity. The offer I have received from a leading men's magazine to write about the World Cup is not one I can easily refuse. I have, as my accountant puts it, an adverse financial situation brought on by an acrimonious divorce and the decision of my wife to screw me for every peso I've got. I would have preferred to stay away from a city that I always feared would stir up memories too easily, of a kind one would have preferred forgotten, or at least softened by the passage of time. A city where the diary I wrote has not been revisited until today . . .

It was late one night in May 1978, that Luis, Elena, and I sat in our favourite Paris bar – Le Piano Vache on the Rue Laplace – planning to do what we had come to make a habit of on Saturdays – get pissed and argue about politics and life in general. But the evening ended on a note which may have been foretold but which none of us predicted.

Various factors had made this inevitable and I mention them in no particular order for even twenty years on my memory still plays tricks with me, such was the trauma we collectively lived that summer. For starters this was Paris, the capital of politics par excellence you might say, where locals and foreigners had made a habit of changing history. There was a palpable buzz around the place on this the tenth anniversary year of the student and worker riots that for a brief but wonderful moment had sent the political establishment diving for cover, just as Peron had managed to do in Argentina.

The three of us were also Argentines brought together with the instinct of cultural self-preservation that comes with exile. Luis and I were mates from childhood. We'd decided to head for Europe in 1975 when Lopez Rega's fascists started to purge the Peronist movement of 'subversive infiltration'. We knew it was only a matter of time before the military stepped in again and then the shit would really hit the fan.

I'd met Elena before Luis although much later Luis would swear he'd seen her first in Buenos Aires playing tennis in the university playground. She and I found ourselves, as chance would have it, on the same TV show – one of those late-night ones the masses don't bother watching. A French publisher was launching my *History of the Tango* and I was there to talk about the brothels of Buenos Aires, Hollywood, and of course Paris. Elena had recently arrived from Argentina after being released from prison. The military junta which had come to power in March 1976 had decided to let her go in an act of uncharacteristic clemency largely forced upon them by an uncle of hers who happened to work in the US embassy.

On that TV show Elena gave a graphic account of how she had been abused and tortured in the cells the military had set up in the Navy's Engineering School. She talked too of dozens of other prisoners who had been injected with tranquillizers before being taken off in helicopters and thrown in the River Plate. Shit, I'd thought to myself, the same River Plate which had given its name to the stadium where Luis and I had once seen our team Boca Juniors suffer one of its most crushing defeats.

Afterwards she accepted when I asked whether she wanted to go for a drink. Through a mixture of guilt and lust at first sight Elena and I became lovers that night.

Which brings me back to football and that discussion the three of us had in that bar early in May 1978. You see, football and Boca were really what had made Luis and me good mates. And now football was to change us for ever, not just Luis and me, but the three of us.

I blame Elena for bringing football into a conversation that had initially focused on the various 'acts' that were being arranged in the Sorbonne to mark the spirit of '68. She had drawn a contrast with her uncle and aunt who were visiting Paris and who she'd seen that afternoon. 'You know all they could think of talking to me about was how excited everyone was with the arrangements of the World Cup, and how cheap Paris was compared to Buenos Aires,' Elena said. She was drinking whiskey as she always did, dark and mournful and, oh so beautiful. In her presence I still felt I could say and do anything, but somehow everything would stem from and return to her. I was utterly in love. Unthinkingly I thought football because, before Elena, the only true happiness I had ever really experienced had been in my childhood, watching Boca in La Bombonera, clutching my dad's hand. Luis had also come from a Boca family, which is how we became really good mates, the two dads and two sons joining up every Sunday Boca played at home.

In our Paris exile, however, football had gradually ceased to be the binding element of our friendship, and instead an increasing point of division. Luis had got heavily immersed in the politics of exile – plotting the junta's overthrow in endless meetings with fellow revolutionaries from Nicaragua and the Sorbonne. I'd first got immersed with the book, and then with Elena who seemed to ensure that we both underwent a physical and emotional transformation whenever we shared a bed.

But while football ceased to be my overriding passion, it never went out of my life. I was helped in this by Elena who in spite of hating the sport tolerated my love of it. On Thursday nights I'd play five-a-side with a group of South American exiles, and I'd make a point of keeping a check on the football scores back home thanks to an Argentine I knew who worked at a news agency. It was through him that I heard the remarkable story of Perico Perez, the goalkeeper and leader of the union of footballers. Boca offered him a huge contract but he turned it down when the club's directors insisted that he de-unionise. Perez had said to the Boca manager, Lorenzo: 'You say you want someone with a strong personality to play for you, but if I accepted your club's conditions, I'd feel neutered as a person.' It's people like Perez that keep alive one's love for the game.

*   *   *

And there was something in that tenth anniversary of '68, in the hidden empty spaces of exile, of time past and passing, and uncertain future, that sparked off a longing for the excitement of the game, for the sense of being there, submerged in the tribal awakening of the fans.

In the bar that night football temporarily reclaimed me when, after the sixth beer, I stood looking down at Luis and Elena at the table and said: 'You know, I've been thinking – why don't the three of us fly to BA for the finals?' There was a terrible silence then as Elena and Luis looked at me as if I'd temporarily gone loopy. And I guess that moment was the beginning of the definitive end for the three of us as a team.

'What are you saying, Juan, you son of a bitch – have you forgotten what's going on in our country? Have you forgotten what they did to Elena?' Luis had grabbed me by the collar and I thought was going to biff me one there and then. Elena started shaking as she always did at the slightest suggestion of violence. Luis and I both apologised, and said we'd calm down, but of course we didn't and Elena got up and left. By then I was too drunk and too angry to care either way.

I sat down and drank my beer, then held Luis as he tried to leave. 'Hang on here, Luis, we Argentines deserve a bit of fun after all these years. I mean is it fair to deny those people you and I used to share the terraces with the joy of seeing their players take on the best in the world and maybe win? Do you think Kempes and Maradona care a shit about the junta? They want to play football and millions of Argentines want to watch it.'

I offered Luis my last Gitane as a peace offering, but he pushed me away. 'You know, Juan, I don't know what makes me feel more sick. What you've just said or what our so called "government-in-exile" had endorsed and what I heard repeated by one of those so called revolutionary Peronists at the meeting the other day. "The World Cup in Argentina will be transformed into a truly people's festival. Thanks to the heroic efforts of our comrades we shall make sure that it becomes also a giant press conference to inform the world of the tragedy which our people are suffering."'

There had been others at that meeting – none of them Argentine – who had taken Luis's position that the World Cup should be boycotted. 'These were Germans, Frenchmen, Italians, Englishmen,' Luis remembered, 'who had no problems with agreeing with me. Because for a decent European, with a good sense of history, it's sheer complicity to allow an international sports festival to take place next to a concentration camp. But somehow it's us Argentines, us football-fanatical Argentines, that manage to forget what only happened yesterday. I don't call that sport, Juan, I call that fascism.'

I looked at Luis and felt sorry for him, for the way that somehow politics had soured what had once been his one enjoyment in life. 'I think you're wrong, mate, and I hope to be able to say you were when I get back,' I said to him when we left the bar in the early hours of the morning. By then I had begun to feel a familiar longing for Elena.

The next afternoon, I was nursing a hang-over while walking with Elena in the Tuileries gardens. It was here, amidst the old statues, that we always came whenever we needed to settle whatever turbulence had entered our relationship. It was a warm spring day. A sense of life awakening hung in the air. You could smell the flowers and hear the bird song. We sat on a bench and watched a group of children playing with the small sailing boats on the pond. 'You know, I've been thinking about last night,' Elena said, breaking the silence which had bound us for a while. 'There's something Camus wrote about football once. For him, football was where he got back in touch with his own humanity. Those ninety minutes was life played out in all its extremes, its hopes and failures. Men cry at football.' My head was trying to make sense of what she was saying. She continued. 'What I'm trying to say, Juan, is that maybe I don't agree with you but I think I do understand what you're doing.'

Later that evening I took the train to Charles de Gaulle and caught the plane to Buenos Aires.

Waiting in the queue at the immigration desk at Ezeiza airport, I broke out in a cold sweat. On the plane my mood had swung between excitement and panic, part of me joyous with the anticipation of coming home, part of me no longer sure where home was any more. The queue seemed interminable. The yellow line at the end of it with the sign 'DO NOT MOVE BEYOND THIS POINT UNTIL SUMMONED' freshly painted. I had broken no law in my country or in anybody else's, and yet I knew that the status of exile marked me out as a potential subversive. The woman immigration officer checked me out with cold efficiency, matching my face with the photograph while eyeing a list to the side of the desk in front of her.

I'd read in the French newspapers that all the junta wanted was for the World Cup to pass off without incident and to impress foreign sports writers there was no need to engage in politics. All the talk of the disappeared belonged to a campaign by 'international Marxism' to unfairly discredit the greatest sporting event in the world. A military spokesman, General Omar Riveros, had told a French journalist: 'This talk that we are torturing prisoners is bullshit. They commit suicide before we touch them.' Bullshit, yes, bullshit, that's what it was.

I looked at the woman immigration officer looking at me. 'I hope we win,' I said, forcing a smile. She smiled too, only her mouth was twisted, stressed with her own repression. 'Ah, so you've come to see the Championship. We'll make sure you enjoy the football, Señor Aranda,' she said, stamping my entry card and waving me on. I was no longer an exile but a free citizen of the universe of football.

If only memory was so simple. Ezeiza. Sure, the word would in a matter of days be stamped on thousands of plane tickets and foreign passports, just another port of entry to which the universal fan could point in his old age and tell his grandchildren – 'I was there.' But to a part of me, the place was still synonymous with death. As the taxi took me from the airport, past the military check points, and along the motorway to the city, I looked out across the flat countryside – groups of cattle grazing on the pampas – and remembered how it was here that the thought of leaving Argentina had first been lodged in me, five years earlier.

On June 20th 1973, I had joined thousands of other students who had come to the airport to greet Peron's return from exile in Madrid. Things were looking up. After years of military govern-ments, there was a revolutionary atmosphere in the air as if Evita had risen from the dead. We danced in the streets, we danced in the stadiums. Football had become fun again. This Marxist coach called Cesar Menotti, an ex Boca player, was part of our movement, transforming Huracan club into a class act that struck us as pure poetry. That was the year Menotti told Houseman: 'When you go out and play, invent your game. It has to be like no one's been taught before.'

We were still dancing when the first shots were fired at us by Lopez-Rega's right-wing fascists. They wounded my mate Mariano in the leg. Then civil war broke out. Right-wing Peronist against left-wing Peronist and anyone else who happened to be around caught in the middle. The ensuing 'battle' around Ezeiza was bloody and tribal, horrific in its cruelty. Dozens killed. Hun-dreds wounded. Those captured by one band or the other were beaten up, or tortured, then shot. I just remember running for my life across those fields in the midst of gunshots and screams and the smell of burning flesh. Later, in the university, they claimed it was at Ezeiza, in the midst of the 'biggest popular mobilisation in Argentine history', that the death squads were born.

There seemed so much of Buenos Aires that seemed familiar, and yet so much that seemed to have gone beyond me. Elena had warned me that an exile's reunion with the city of the past is like the return of a divorcee to the former family home. I found familiarity in the smell of charcoaled meat, in the hissing of coffee machines. I was reminded of how deliberately parts of the city, built at the turn of the century, had tried to ape Paris with its palatial residences and generous avenues. But gone were the graffiti we had painted on the walls. Gone the posters of Che Guevara and the buskers in the streets. Instead there were giant billboards claiming that 25 million Argentines – the entire population – were united behind the great enterprise of winning the World Cup. There were also colour TVs, a pro junta propaganda spot interrupting each programme. It flashed incessantly through the shop windows in Calle Florida and from the sitting rooms of the apartment blocks in Avenida Libertador. What people really thought and felt was hard to fathom at first amidst the urban order and prosperity. The World Cup symbol was a caricature of a gaucho sporting the Argentine colours. But no one seemed to be laughing any more. Argentina, or so it seemed to me on arrival, had become a country of public posturing and terrible unspoken secrets. The only subject people seemed free to talk about was football.

On my first night in the city I sat drinking some beers in a cafe on the Avenida Corrientes with Roberto. It was his flat I had arranged to stay in for the duration of my visit, and it was thanks to him that I had secured tickets for some of the matches. An old friend from university, Roberto was one of the few members of my generation who had managed to adapt to the times. During the heady revolutionary days of '73 he had been literary editor of one of the country's leading newspapers. Then a week before the coup in March 1976 he had turned sports writer, securing a regular beat on the trail of Boca and the national squad. Roberto had always hated the idea of exile, and considered his betrayal of our cause a lesser form of cowardice. For weeks now Roberto had been absorbed in following Cesar Menotti prepare a team capable of winning the World Cup. El Flaco was still a hero as far as he was concerned. A radio reporter had told Roberto that Menotti had secretly told his players to go out and play for the people not the junta.

I asked Roberto whether he thought we'd win the Cup. 'I don't think El Flaco has a choice,' Roberto answered, before lowering his voice. 'If he doesn't the junta will shoot him.' 'Pity Maradona's been dropped from the team. People are beginning to talk about him in Europe, you know,' I said. 'Tell you the truth, Juan, the team's pretty good without him. Di Stefano calls Kempes "the beautiful machine".'

For over an hour Roberto and I talked and argued football – players, tactics, teams – the danger of playing against Platini's France and the Italians in the opening group, the unpredictability of the Brazilians, the pity, from a purely competitive point of view, that Cruyff and Beckenbauer weren't turning up . . . until something happened that made me change the subject: I heard the sound of a police siren out in the city somewhere, followed by the distant sound of gunfire. 'Well, Roberto mate, tell me, what it's really like here? The junta says the French press have got it all wrong and that we exiles have been putting out a bunch of lies. Is that true?' I asked.

Roberto fell silent, and looked discreetly around the room before saying: 'Shit, man, you can't imagine what it's like – not being able to write about anything but football – the same words and phrases going round and round to describe this move or that – and you know that, yes, people are being tortured and killed. At night I go to bed, twisted inside, my brain breaking out in horrors. I have panic attacks. The country's turned into a giant fucking circus – footballers surrounded by soldiers and hacks, and death camps – out of sight – beneath the stadiums . . .'

'What's happened to Pablo?' I asked.

When Roberto told me he had disappeared I realised that I had asked the question already knowing the answer. Pablo and Roberto had been in the demonstration at Ezeiza, but of the three of us Pablo alone had afterwards declared himself determined to carry on the struggle in Argentina. The day I left for France, we hugged each other like true brothers. I couldn't bring myself to tell him my certainty that I would never see him again.

On my second day back in Argentina I went to Pablo's family home – a fourth-floor flat on the Avenida de Santa Fe where he'd lived with his parents ever since he was a kid. Before the bus ride, I bought the latest issue of *Grafico* to check out the latest football news and comment. There were interviews with Menotti and with Kempes, meticulous profiles of Fillol, Ardiles, and Houseman, dozens of colour photographs of the team at practice and at play. I turned the pages quickly, absorbing the pictures of my football heroes with the same frenzy I had once devoted to the pages of pornographic magazines during the early days of solitude in Paris. On one page there was a long editorial, praising the organisation of the World Cup of Peace, as General Videla had called it. I was struck by these lines: '. . . This tournament is showing the world the reality of our country and its capacity to do things with responsibility and to do important things well . . . Journalists who for months have been organising a campaign of lies against us should take note . . .'

I was met by Pablo's father, Ernesto. He had aged a great deal since I'd last seen him. He greeted me with a prolonged embrace which had us both in tears. Then he took me through the long dark corridor of the flat, head bowed, and dragging his feet to the room where Pablo had once studied for his exams. The room was exactly as I remembered it – books and records and an old tea bowl on the coffee table by the sofa where Pablo and I had sat smoking into the early hours. In the instant I felt Pablo's presence,

I also recognised his irretrievable absence. 'They broke through the front door at three-thirty in the morning,' Ernesto told me. 'There were about twenty men dressed in civilian clothes, led by a man who shouted that he was a police officer and that this was a raid. One pulled my wife screaming from the bed, while three others pushed me against the wall and pinned me there. "Shut your mouth, bitch," I heard one of them say to my wife, while the rest went through the rooms, breaking and tearing things as they went, until they found what they were looking for. I heard Pablo's cries of pain and their curses, and then the sound of his body being dragged along the corridor, and the front door opening and slamming shut, and the leader of the pack shout to the others that it was all done and that they had got their shitface subversive.'

Later Ernesto told me how thanks to a friend of a friend of a general he had subsequently been told that Pablo had been taken to a secret cell the navy had in the northern suburbs. From there he had been transferred to the Navy's Engineering School.

'Have you seen him?' I asked. 'Seen him?' Ernesto said, 'They won't even admit that he has ever existed.'

We were alone, the old man and I. Pablo's mother had not made an appearance since my arrival. 'Where is Celia?' I asked.

'She is where she always is on a Thursday these days – outside the Presidential palace in the Plaza de Mayo, calling out for her son.'

Celia was wearing a white scarf tied around her head. She held a poster-size photograph of Pablo. Together with a small group of women she was walking slowly round the gardens of the square in dignified protest. 'Where are our husbands? Where are our children? The disappeared, tell us where they are?' they chanted.

Two van-loads of police arrived, one taking up position outside the presidential palace, the other creating an outside circle round the demonstration. A French television crew arrived and started filming. As they did so another group of civilians – all men dressed smartly in winter coats – appeared from nowhere and crowded round the camera. 'Argentina, Argentina, Argentina,' they cried. As I watched the scene, a policeman came over and told me to move on. I could see Celia and the other women being insulted by the group of men: 'Antipatriotic bitches! Traitors of shit!'

As I walked away, I felt in my pocket for the tickets to the game. I wanted to feel I was still alive.

My diary stops that afternoon in the Plaza de Mayo. My memory is prompted by a video I bought the other day in a shop off the Charing Cross Road, but only prompted. For the English commentary seems dislocated and the action anaesthetised of any feeling. And I am trying to recover something of what I felt that June of 1978, not snapshots of another World Cup. So let us try to remember together, what it was like when at fifteen hundred hours, the tournament opened in the River Plate Stadium . . .

It is something like this . . . The world trembles beneath my feet, the collective roar rises from deep within the earth, the sky showers white paper, my heart goes out of my mouth and surfs the tribal wave – ARGENTINA, ARGENTINA, ARGENTINA. I am there with everybody else shouting it, crying it, jumping on my feet as if the stadium were a magic castle. I am thrilled.

Out they come, our players, like uncaged gladiators fighting for their freedom, fighting for our freedom, declaring their right to 'invent'. And this they do without a doubt. Each pass, each run, each touch and strike, expresses a lightness of being that has been purged from our streets. And we are running with them, savouring the poetry of invention. And all the while the junta – the same junta that has managed so effectively to eradicate life from our country – stands across the pitch from me – Massera, Videla, Agosti, stuffed eagles in their winter trench coats, with the emotion of statues. During ninety minutes of football, they are overtaken and eclipsed. They have come not to live the game but to assure themselves of victory.

But they are powerless.

And it is like that for much of the tournament. Local winter but so warm, brother, so warm. Some of our players have long hair. Some let their socks fall round their ankles. Some are unshaven. They are eleven beautiful free individuals struck by El Flaco's magic spell. And of the eleven, one seems to be in full flight for most of the time, like an angel of God. His name is Mario Kempes.

'El que no baile es un holades' – 'He who does not dance is a Dutchman' – and we are all dancing together, knowing that El Flaco's wizardry will cast the ultimate spell. And Kempes has taken up the ball and is flying once again, a crazy, crazy, angel, swerving this way and that, taking us with him all the time, all the way into the Dutch goal. In my mind Kempes is still running with outstretched arms when Bertoni scores the third. They are part of the same movement – that GOOOOOAL echoing through the heavens with the certainty that the Cup is ours. And now I am hugging the old man next to me, unknown to me at the start of the match, but now transformed into the best friend I have been seeking since childhood. We are crying our hearts out, dragged out through the darkness, light breaking out everywhere, joy, sheer joy . . .

I would like to tell you that this is how it ended, that here memory accommodated my simple desire to be, that this was real life. Well it could have been like this had I not decided, after the game, to linger rather than allow myself to be swept along by the collective ecstasy, the cacophany of car horns, trumpets, crackers, Freddie Mercury on the radio singing *We are the Champions*. You have to understand that this lingering had nothing to do with a wish to exclude myself from my tribe. Quite the opposite, I lingered because quite soon after that lengthy embrace with the old man I was taken by a terrible longing to share the moment with Elena. I hung around long enough to find a telephone booth that was empty and telephoned Elena's flat in Paris. It was Luis who answered the phone. He listened silently while for about a minute I tried to convey the extraordinary scene I had experienced in the stadium. Then Elena interrupted, telling me to stop it.

'Look, Juan, you don't understand. We don't want to know. And if you knew what's been happening you wouldn't want to tell us.'

That is not quite how the conversation went but it is how memory has reduced it. I do remember the emptiness of the street outside when I eventually left the booth. I remember too the sound of a helicopter hovering somewhere near the river.

My Back Pages

Steve Grant

When JFK got shot I was working in a supermarket. When Elvis died I was in the bath. When John Lennon got shot I heard it over breakfast, listening with my then wife who was an early Beatles screamer and still kept the programmes.

Can't remember much else that's headline global: except World Cups. It might have something to do with the fact that my son was born the day that Holland beat Italy and Brazil beat Peru in the 1978 World Cup finals. It was half-time across the world in Argentina. I got the phone call as the Italians had gone 1-0 up. It was a great time: we'd moved into our first home; I'd been the first ever staff recipient of paternity leave, seven weeks off with full pay, such a newsworthy concept that Radio 4 came round to do a story, a delightful lady who now does the Royals on BBC1 and sometimes presents the *Nine O'Clock News*. 'It's such a godsend that he's around,' the wife said. On air. Then she was taken in after our son began his lifetime career of only doing something when he feels ready, alarmingly overdue, with induction, inducement – sounds like a bung, doesn't it? – a serious option. Our daughter was packed off to the in-laws, and I began a period of work-leave in which I would battle clownishly with the pelmets, which had more holes in them than Dutch Schultz by the time the curtains went up, the secondhand Ascot in the kitchen, the wiring, the garden, the carpeting, a year's supply of beer and baby food, and a World Cup made doubly palatable by the absence of England (no nerves, you see) and the comic downfall of the cocky Jocks of Allie's Tartan Army.

So it seemed natural to shoot down to the hospital, hang around uselessly for the birth, think that he'd been born dead before realising that the sucker registering his heartbeat had come off at the climax of labour, ogle the afterbirth, hear the kid scream 'Gooooall' after the standard tap on the arse, and return home in time for another feast of footie. Actually the Brazil-Peru game wasn't a classic and the Brazilians were later stitched up by the host nation who beat Peru by a sombrero full of goals in what ranks as the shadiest contest ever played in world soccer. But I was mightily chuffed to hear that the Dutch had beaten the Italians, 2-1. It was pretty much the perfect day.

All my World Cups are thus neatly divided into pre- and post-parenthood. In 1974 I was single and dividing my time between sports broadcasting for a local radio station and working for a theatre magazine buried in the basement of a Victorian block opposite New Scotland Yard. The editor and I drank in the same pub as the cops and, this being at the height of the first mainland IRA bombing campaign, we couldn't understand why they weren't targeting us rather than the usual hapless cleaner who'd lose her fingers when she turned up to Sanilav the bogs of some Mayfair eaterie. Terrorism courtesy of Egon Ronay. The ed (now a major national critic) and I were united not just by the theatre but by our status as lone football fans and token heterosexuals in a place that was otherwise queer down to the office boy. We shared a tiny, chaotic office with another arts mag, the editor of which made Julian Clary look like Tommy Lee Jones and who would delight in ringing up a boyfriend on SwissAir with obscene details of his latest conquest, delivered at maximum volume. My house name was 'Solzhenitsyn'. I've had worse.

One evening, as I was off to Selhurst Park to cover a cup replay, I was rung by our secretary in the next room, literally feet away with an adjoining door. He let out a pitiful wail. I went through and found him standing on top of his desk, shaking and blubbering and pointing at the floor. Drew, let us so name him, couldn't leave the mag and go home because of this supposedly giant spider which was crawling around among the yellowing back copies of *Playbill* and *Theatre Quarterly*. I spent the next twenty minutes tracking down Mr Itsy Bitsy, finally locating the hairy, zigzagging fucker by the waste bin and despatching him painlessly but violently with the heel of my shoe. 'You didn't have to murder him,' blubbed Drew. When I got to Crystal Palace, the match had already begun and my phone wouldn't work. When I finally got through to the studio, I was apoplectic. They accused me afterwards of being drunk. Fat chance. But I couldn't really tell them that I'd been engaged in hit-man duties on an arachnid for an ungrateful, cringeing screamer.

Arts and sports. It could have gone either way: the radio stuff was knockabout chaos in the station's first year. Our boss, a guy called Ian Marshall, was a wonderful maverick, now long dead, who once went in to prepare an hour-long magazine programme and realised that his watch had stopped and it was about to start. He employed his tailor to go to Craven Cottage and his match report so incensed the then manager that he actually flew up to the press box to confront the sad seamster, who returned later to deliver an abject reassessment of Fulham as the nearest thing to Real Madrid that London had ever seen. We were always falling about during phone-ins ('Have any of the panel seen Villa this season?' 'Eeer, no, sorry.'). There were on-air verbal punch-ups and real fisticuffs afterwards at a time when Danny Baker was still lining up for his free school pinta and having his head searched for nits. I remember a particularly nasty row between two reporters as to whether Spurs' then assistant manager Eddie Bailey was or wasn't 'a complete plank'. We didn't know shit, but the show was giddy and irreverent and a mile away from the standard pipe-and-trenchcoat cobblers of the time.

In the holiday summer of 1974, there was lots of work to be had: I wrote and presented the weekly sports magazine programme. Don't say much about the World Cup, they said, so I merely ended the broadcast with an afterthought. 'Oh yes, and in that other competition that begins this week in Germany, my prediction: West Germany 2, Holland 1.' It was only after the final had ended that I realised I'd made one of the most amazing predictions. OK, so it wasn't Wales 9, Central African Republic 5, but the two correct teams, the correct score. Luckily, all tapes were 'top and tailed', filed with the first and last sentences as reference points. This was long before betting on results became a national pastime but I could at least bask in the station recognition that came on that night's news. 'Our man tipped the outcome before the competition even started.' Problem is, a week later they fired me. Problem is, I still wish I'd put that bet on.

This is a true story: please go immediately to London Weekend Television, cover the friendly between England and Yugoslavia in Belgrade, and, while not actually fibbing, try to give the impression that you're at the ground. The catch was that when I arrived in the completely deserted studio there was a massive bank of thirty television screens, no sound at all, and a travelogue about the wonders of Belgrade in progress. No sound. The teams flashed up: I managed the England line-up, but let me tell you that it is not wise to start your international football broadcasting career with Balkanites whose surnames remind me to this day of the joke about the Polish guy who goes to the opticians. 'Can you read the bottom line?' 'Read it? I know him.' Yugoslavian TV captions didn't help much: while I was trying to sort out my Stalectitovics from my Stalectmitocics, the phone rang. It wasn't the boys in the studio but the highly respected world soccer expert Eric Batty who was doing a piece for the *Evening Standard* and wanted to know the line-ups. Nobody had told me he was going to call. I gave him nine Yugoslavian names. 'You have given me nine names,' he explained patiently. I put the phone down.

There was worse to come. My early reports were somewhat rudimentary: 'Well, it's a balmy seventy-five here in beautiful Belgrade and though the Slavs are pressing, England are holding their end up well. Popic [I'm making him up, but I'm still too terrified to look up the details in Rothman's] is causing a lot of problems for our midfield.' Of course, it transpired that 'Popic' was their goalie . . . It happened to be pretty balmy in that studio as well. Unpeopled and silent as the grave, it still had a healthy supply of jugged water. I've always been a perspirer and soon a combination of nerves and heat had me guzzling. Before long I needed the toilet. Where was the toilet? Could I hang on? No I couldn't. I left my post for a piss. When I returned, around five minutes later and with boots well splashed, I continued to relay the score as 0-0. Then the Yugos actually had the decency to flash up a scoreline: they had, in fact, been leading, probably courtesy of a goal by Slobodan Milosevic, by 1-0. So I hung on into the second half, but have you ever noticed that when you drink a lot, one wee suddenly becomes two, ah sweet, maybe Annie Lennox should write a song about it. So I rushed limply out again, got my todger back inside my trousers ten seconds before I'd actually finished, and returned in a rapidly cooling pool of clamminess to predict that it looked all over for our boys. And of course our boys had gone and equalised while I was away in the carzey for the second time. As well as managing to give the wrong score for most of the ninety minutes, my work in the field of foreign pronunciation was being keenly noted by the station's chief executive who just happened to have dropped in and was listening to the entire bloody fiasco in his suite. Every time I hear Barry Davies say 'Shol-sheeee-yarrrr-aah' these days, I reach for my gun. And my broadcasting career never really recovered: the next friendly they offered me was in Cambodia . . .

P-F, post-fatherhood, I've had problems of a very different sort. They don't change the dates of World Cups and my son's birthday, which is also the same day as Operation Barbarossa, when the Germans invaded the Soviet Union with more than Uwe Seeler, has a habit of coinciding with national frenzy. He was eight on the day that Argentina beat us 2-1 in Mexico, and his children's party was somewhat marred by my chucking a plateful of jelly at the screen when Maradona hand-balled the Argies into the lead. Later I rang up the Tunisian Embassy to tell them that (a) I would never holiday there again; and (b) I hoped that Algeria would soon invade them; (c) one of their camels once disgracefully threw me on my arse; (d) couscous, their national dish, was the Arab equivalent of Irish stew; and (e) their linesman, who didn't flag for the foul, should be first stuffed full of (d) and then roundly sodomised by one of (c)'s cousins. It's rough on my son, though: he's never really taken to sport, although he tried, God love him, and at the time he was young enough to be traumatised by his dad's alarming transformation into this foul-mouthed jack-in-a-box, purring 'Yes, what a lovely card' and 'Ooooh, a *Star Wars* toy, how peachy', while at the same time howling at the set and darting round piles of sarnies and crisps to catch a glimpse of the genius dwarf scoring an amazing second goal, Lineker pulling one back and then being denied at the death by a goal-line interception, after Barnes's deep cross, that I still can't credit after the thousandth video replay. At the time, all the New Age footie fans of my acquaintance deemed it a just score, that the Argentinians were the better team anyway. Bullshit. Had that second goal gone in, we would have walked it in extra time, beaten Belgium and then no doubt been robbed by the Germans in the final.

Luckily he was too young to remember much about 1982, which was the year his parents split up. We made a pact that I wouldn't actually leave until after the finals. It was something to look forward to, and of course something to savour at a time when things had got decidedly messy: my big mistake was taking the dartboard into the bedroom. My attempts at a double one made a particularly bad impression on the wallpaper. He kept me company; we played and I settled down as England began like a train, three wins out of three in the qualifying group, Robson's seventeenth-second goal against France, and surely we could do something here. But no. People usually forget that the World Cup is a tournament. OK, so often the best side wins, but more often it doesn't go to plan. Teams peak too early, preliminary matches don't run to form, injuries and luck are always a factor. England took part in a one-off and silly round of three-way matches. We faced the hosts, Spain, and the deadly Germans; OK, so the eventual winners Italy had to beat both Argentina and Brazil but then the Azzurri should have gone out in the first phase and would have done if a linesman hadn't flagged for a perfectly good goal scored by Cameroon. Because there was no knockout, England reverted to type, managed two 0-0 draws and went home undefeated and without a sniff of the trophy. We needed to beat Spain by two goals in the last match and I can still remember Kevin Keegan's miss with a close-range header, this bepermed superstar who my children pointed at, enraptured, because of his sterling work in the cereals-modelling department. It gets a bit wanky, sometimes, relating football to yer actual sweaty real life: but only the people who don't understand it really think so. Like JFK, Elvis and John Lennon, it's always there, always this pulsing riff playing in the background. Maybe if Keegan and Brooking had scored, then . . . well . . . maybe not.

In 1990, it was my daughter's turn. She *is* a sports nut. When Germany played us in the semi-finals of 1990 we'd had tickets for the Rolling Stones at Wembley. I'd first seen the Stones in 1963 when my English master actually called them 'antichrists' and the entire lower sixth laughed like a drain; Brian Jones sat in a chair; Mick Jagger wore a Fair Isle sweater; Keith Richards still looked drop-dead cool in a black leather jacket; and Watts and Wyman were, well yeah . . . I'm sure they were there as well. The Stones ripped into Chuck Berry's 'Talkin' 'Bout You', followed with 'Mona' and 'Cops and Robbers' and climaxed their set with their cover of the Beatles' 'I Wanna Be Your Man'. For the first and last time, at the Dunstable California Ballroom anyway, women took their dresses off and danced in their slips on tables and chairs. Oh, damn them slips! I'd even got to interview old rubber lips himself in 1989, and got on well apart from his tendency to head for the door every time you paused for breath. The Stones were even going through a revival period, back to basics with new technology attached and not so much of that aimless seventies gunk that only serial killers danced to: but no, England were playing Germany in the semi-finals of the World Cup.

Isn't it funny that our proudest memories are of England teams that lost? The greatest England side ever outplaying Brazil in 1970, hitting the bar, missing an open goal, pulling off the greatest save in the history of the game, and losing 1-0, albeit to a goal from Jairzinho that still ranks among my favourites. Tostao's swerve, Pelé's defence-destroying side-foot, and the winger's glorious, unanswerable cross-shot and whooping, ecstatic run to the bench. Or the quarter-final defeat in the same year, the heat and altitude of Leon unbearable, Banksie crocked with a mysterious stomach ailment, England 2-0 up and cruising, and then Beckenbauer, Seeler, Müller, and 3-2 to the Hun. I watched that at home with my parents, and never was there so much misery in one household. It's rumoured that after the contest a German journalist shouted: 'We've beaten you at your national game!' And the great Geoffrey Green of the *Times* replied: 'Yes, and we've beaten you at yours. Twice.' God, I hope it really happened, but then what if it didn't? As the man said in that John Ford western: print the legend. And anyway I'll not hear a bad word to this day about the Kaiser. One of the most promising features of the present national set-up is that Glenn Hoddle speaks English almost as well as Franz Beckenbauer.

When England lost in Turin that night, we all cried. An Australian friend rang up from Majorca the second the final whistle sounded. He was in a bar surrounded by Germans, pissed as a fart, obviously touched – as much as any Australian male who's downed seventeen jugs of Sangria can be. 'You stuffed 'em, Grant, you fucking stuffed 'em. I've been telling that to these Krauts, they thought they were gonna walk it and they've been shitting themselves for two hours.' I put the phone down on him as well. But later I came to appreciate the thought.

As for my son, the agonies continue: he was eighteen on the day that England played Spain in the quarter-finals of Euro '96. We were lucky then, in fact it's arguable that the Spaniards were robbed. When Seaman made that last penalty shoot-out save, we hugged each other like long-lost team-mates. I could feel his body shaking with relief. And there was still time enough left to party, back at his home, which was once my home, with his mother and sister downstairs, all of us still connected, waiting to join in the celebration.

Something's Coming Home

Chaz Brenchley

They made us walk, to prove that we were healthy.

Diseases of the blood, they said, *diseases of the night*. The new president had forbidden those his country; and so we must walk, a trek of fifty miles, and so we were watched all the way. Even in the dark, especially in the dark they watched us from helicopter-lightships like clattering moons, milk-bright and deadly. Dazzled, we squinted up with weeping eyes unshaded, to show how well we were.

By day trucks rumbled past us, coming and going. Men and boys, in uniforms and rags: their eyes, their guns watched us. Neither spoke, nor we to them. We walked.

The road, the air was kerosene and dust; the rains were late again, and might not come now. Fields cropped nothing. We carried husks of maize, and chewed dry grains. A jerrycan of water was rare wealth, liquidity.

At night we burned what we could find, slept little, welcomed strangers to our fires. Football was the lingua franca, our common currency, reliable and safe. Only the World Cup, nothing closer to any thought of home. There if anywhere, we thought, we could be easy with each other. This old country had a new name and no flag yet; how could they or any of their spies accuse us of disloyalty, where there was no history and nothing to dishonour?

So we sat in the flamelight and talked of Pelé in '58, in '62, in '70. We had not seen; that did not stop us talking. Shadows were safer, ghost conversations about ghosts. We did not touch each other.

• Chaz Brenchley

Sometimes the young would speak of this year's Cup, a new Pelé; a ghost made flesh? we asked, and laughed at them. We who knew ghosts, who walked that haunted road and never looked over our shoulders: we had known ghost-houses too, villas with peeling paintwork and the smells of terror and death within, bodies hung or dumped outside the door.

Laughed less when they went on talking, when they spoke of one team, one country's strength and another's decay. *Too close to home*, we thought, we who were wise or frightened. Football is only a disguise if you will use it so; like anything, used otherwise it could be code or truth. Any man sat by the fire there, any woman shuffling in the shadows behind could turn spy or informer for a handful of meal, could be turned already; it was foolish even to sound as though they might be speaking secrets.

Even the children we could not trust, even those we carried because they could not walk. Drum bellies and drumstick ribs, big eyes and empty mouths, silent as their dangling feet were still: they should be playing Pelé, kicking ragballs in the dust. They should not look so sick. Stupid to be a child and look sick, where adults must march to demonstrate their health. Who knew what such a child might not offer to an armed man at a roadblock, to say the blood was not bad but only thinned as the body was?

All we could offer to the children was a handful of coarse paste night and morning, with lies for salt. *Here, eat, this will make you strong again, Look, see, that big plane high above us, do you hear its roar? That's the team, your favourite team, flying to victory. All your heroes, see them look down now, see them wave at you?*

They saw little, nothing some: their eyes were filmed and failing. But they had ears, they listened still; they had tongues, although they might not use them. Who could trust a child?

The planes carried players in some higher game. The country had only ever made one football hero, and him we might not speak of: he bore the wrong name, the wrong allegiance now, and played

• 134

for a famous club in another land, some other world than this. He had said nothing for years, never touched on home; pray God he would say nothing still. At such a time the world, both worlds might listen, his and ours. It was not his feet that trod this long and breathless road, with the jetscream overhead. His planes did carry footballers.

We carried children, guilt, uncertainty, despair: all hollow. Even hunger is no heavy load where fear grips your hands and binds your tongue, sets stumbles for your feet to find when anyone is watching.

We walked to show our health, but were not healthy. By sun and moon we died, and in their absence: one at my fire, one night. We pulled him quickly from the light, so neither we nor they could see; we said he must be old, too old to march so far.

At the bottom of his bag we found a cloth, broad and long. No one wanted that. In the dark who knew, who could say what flag it might have been? We said we could not see. For safety's sake we wrapped his body in it, laid both in a gully and tipped rocks down until we truly could not.

The helicopters came too late; we had already found our fire before their lights stabbed blindly at the dark. For sure they would not see the body, nor the flag.

Perhaps it was Brazil's, we said aloud and nodded, each to each.

Every Four Years We Become a Nation

Ron Butlin

Like almost everybody else in Scotland I had bought the mug, the T-shirt, got drunk and sang 'Allie's Tartan Army' on the tops of buses. Once again there was hope in Scotland, once again we were on the march. For the first time since last time (RIP Billy Bremner et al) we were a nation once more.

Nationhood is awarded to us every four years. For ninety minutes at a stretch, us raggedy Scotties with a Whitehall father put away our political immaturity and rise above our traditional Scottish heroes who themselves are all children (Peter Pan, Wee McGregor, Oor Wullie). For the brief span between whistle blasts we are adults laying claim to an adulthood that includes the likes of Dalgleish and Law striding into the world arena on our behalf. Boozed and bunneted in front of the TV we watch real heroes, in our name, taking on the Goliaths of every continent. They score goals of contrapuntal elegance that fleetingly partake of the Platonic Ideal 'Goal' (surely Archie Gemmel's timeless sarabande through the Holland defence in '78 cannot have vanished into Nothingness?). Thus, for one moment every four years, the kilted and non-kilted alike, we stand at the very threshold of eternity, with our heads held high.

The moment, of course, passes.

If it was only the Goliaths we had to flatten, we'd win the World Cup every time round. No problem. Unfortunately there's also our fellow Davids (Zaire, Cameroon . . . you name it, we've never scored what's needed. If Estonia had fixed their floodlights, they'd have gone on to fix us). Hardest of all is the struggle with ourselves. It's not a coach the Scottish team needs, but a therapist. Brought up on a diet of historical bungles, betrayals and defeats from the time of William Wallace onwards, there's not one ounce of self-belief in the entire squad. Did Bonnie Prince Charlie, the team captain of our first national away game, get beaten by the English? No, for having reached Derby, he was face to face with possible victory. Instead, such was his fear of the unfamiliar, he turned and legged it back to Scotland for a reassuring home defeat on such massive a scale as to have kept us going nearly to the present day. No matter how loudly the Tartan Army sings of glory, 'deep-down' the boys in blue don't believe a word of it. None of us does. Give us one glimpse of true self-awareness and yet again, in that all-too memorable phrase, we will 'snatch defeat from the jaws of victory'.

So, remember, if you will, the highest point of all our hopes and longings: that game against Peru. We were ahead from early on. And for once we weren't clawing our way back towards defeat; every pass was a masterpiece of precision, every shot on target. Then came the equaliser. No. No. Yes. These were the odds we liked. From Buenos Aires to Bishopriggs we were hoarse, a heartbeat away from cardiac arrest and cheering ourselves tartan. Then it happened. The ultimate miracle. The penalty. This was it. Utter and complete euphoria. We were in, at last. We had to be.

'Deep-down', of course, each one of us knew what was going to happen.

Even as I write this, recalling the quality of that silence as Don Masson prepared to take the penalty, I confess there is a part of me believes that everything since has been a two-second dream. Yes, such is the power of our Scottish schizophrenia that we're still there, holding our breath and watching him amble over to tap it into the onion-bag. So, a few steps and up he goes – and, as we all knew all along, it's the Big Toe to Nowhere. Taking the next twenty years with it.

We were sorry for Don. Who wouldn't be? But the real tragedy of the Scottish people is that any one of us would have done exactly the same. 'Here's our big chance, let's really fuck it up,' says that two-way split to self-destruction, our national psyche. Thereafter, freed from the threat of success, we played like angels in the final match against Holland and, watched over by the dentally challenged spirit of Joe Jordan soaring above the box, we guided ourselves home to another glorious defeat.

It didn't stop there, of course. The next few months revealed to us how it was all part of the Great Plan to secure total oblivion: first, the World Cup, then the Referendum for Scottish Independence. Had Don Masson scored we might have been confronted with the reality of self-determination and the heady prospect of actually growing up. As it was, Don took the kick for us all, and we were safe.

The next twenty years were a kind of Dark Ages of the Scottish Soul. A comforting black hole: Nowheresville, just south of the Arctic Circle, where we could snap and snarl at our fate, while enjoying the security of Immaturity Regained. Our ambassadors, Rab C Nesbitt and Billy Connolly, reinforced our self-image while cocking a snoot, jester-like, at authority; the sweeties they were thrown we knew were being thrown at us, and it made us proud to be recognised for what we were. The media – that soundtrack for those afraid to hear their own voice – spoke on our behalf. Thatcher was loathed in Scotland, yet, due to an incredible combination of Tory arrogance and PR ignorance, she came up here one year to present the SFA cup. From the terraces we gave out a deafening and sustained chorus of 'Fuck Off Maggie!' We knew we were in no danger of being listened to and were chuffed to the sporran to be considered cheeky enough to be sound-brushed out, affording the rest of the country the extraordinary spectacle of the Iron Lady apparently miming her iron smile against an eerie background of televised silence. Though we qualified for the World Cup as regular as clockwork (except in the US – but then, who could take that venue seriously?), we were careful never again to come close to the remotest risk of victory.

A couple of years short of the Millennium and we've taken heart once more. A new generation is born, a new order has come into being. We're going to do things differently this time round: the referendum first, and now the World Cup. Already the signs are promising. Already there's a spring in our step and our eyes are on the horizon. *Trainspotting* has shown us, and the world, what we're capable of. The mugs are being thrown, the songs being written, the bevvy being saved up for. Our clan-chief Craig Brown – the silent man's silent man – issues gnomic statements of cautious optimism.

Let Brazil beware.

Some People Are on the Pitch

Mark Morris

Some People Are on the Pitch

—

The most hated man in Britain, that's what they call me. The *Daily Mirror* ran a poll and 87 per cent of readers said they thought I should get the death penalty. They haven't heard my side of the story, though, have they, they haven't thought to ask *why* I did it? So here I am, setting the record straight, or at least trying to explain.

It all started at the match, of course, everyone knows that. Well all right, they might not have known it at first, not immediately after the deed had been done, but they knew it pretty soon afterwards, thanks to some investigative journalism that, to be frank, didn't require that much investigation. Unless you've been in a coma or on a tropical island or somewhere, you can't fail to have seen the photo of me with my arms around Geoff Hurst on the pitch at Wembley. I was the first one to get to him after he scored his third goal to make it 4-2, after he won the World Cup for England.

Geoff didn't seem to mind at the time. He was grinning all over his sweaty face and he even half-hugged me after I'd hugged him. Then some other England player, Nobby Stiles or Alan Ball or somebody, reached him and lifted him into the air and when that happened I was sort of pushed aside, forgotten. I suppose that could have been the very first thing which made me do what I did. To be honest, I can't remember. It's funny, but sitting here in my cell on this sunny afternoon, writing all this down, I now realise what a strange, twisted journey my mind must have taken, which was caused of course by the stress of everything that resulted from my hugging Geoff. It might sound a bit glib or corny or like I'm passing the buck, but it honestly does seem as though it all happened to somebody else a long time ago, and as though I'm now trying to remember in step-by-step detail what this somebody else told me.

Anyway, as I say, maybe it was partly my congratulations being curtailed by the congratulations of his team-mates, or maybe it wasn't that at all, maybe it was just after, the bobby grabbing my arm above the elbow as I was capering about on the penalty spot, that set me off. Maybe if I had been allowed to finish my celebrations and just run off the pitch back into the crowd none of it would have happened, but then again it probably would have because the pictures of me and Geoff would still have been on the news and in the papers.

The bobby didn't only grab me, he swung me round so fiercely that I lost my footing and ended up with a big green grass stain down my trousers. I looked up at his red, moustached face and he was scowling down at me like I was some child murderer or something. He said, 'That's enough of that sort of behaviour, sonny. Don't you realise the eyes of the whole bloody world are watching you giving this country a bad name?'

'Come on, mate,' I said to him, 'it's not every day that England wins the World Cup.'

'That's no excuse for you to behave like a bloody hooligan,' he said, 'and spoil it for everybody else,' and he pinned my arms behind my back.

As I was led away I remember looking around and seeing the England players hugging each other and the crowd jumping up and down, everybody grinning, and I thought: I'm not spoiling it for anyone. Nobody was going to go home that night and say, 'Well, it *would* have been good if that idiot hadn't hugged Geoff Hurst and danced on the penalty spot.' I suppose I ought to have blamed the bobby for over-reacting, but I suppose, even at the time, part of me must have been thinking: Why doesn't Geoff come over and have a quiet word? I know I certainly thought that afterwards, a few days later. I mean, let's face it, it wouldn't have taken much for him to have said to the bobby, 'Aw, leave it, mate, he's not doing any harm. He just got a bit over excited when I scored my brilliant third goal.'

I was taken to the police station and charged with trespass and making an affray. I was put in a cell and left to stew for a while, and then, about nine o'clock, I was let out and made to fill in a load of forms. I was told I'd have to appear in court – and I feel I ought to point out at this juncture that before all this palaver I'd never broken the law in my life – and then they let me go.

When I got back it was about half past ten. You wouldn't have thought from walking into Linda's parents' house that England had won the World Cup that day, you'd have thought we'd lost about 10-0. Linda and I had been married for nine months at the time and were saving up for our own house. I was saving like mad – I couldn't get out of there quickly enough – but even so, I couldn't see us moving before Christmas.

Linda's parents were church-goers – not that I've got anything against religious types, good God no, but they took that whole Commandments thing very seriously. Thou shalt not dance on the pitch at Wembley like a bloody hooligan even if England *have* won the World Cup: I must have missed that one, but they hadn't.

When I walked into the living room (or lounge as Linda's mum called it) I knew straight away they'd found out. They wouldn't have watched the match – they didn't like football and had disapproved of me going to Wembley that day even though it was the first day out I'd had in ages – so they must have seen it on the news. They were sitting there all prim and stiff and severe-looking as if they'd got broom handles stuffed up their backsides, and Linda was sort of cringing on the settee (sorry: *sofa*). Linda's dad, who looked like an ostrich with a moustache, turned and looked at me as if I was a walking piece of dog dirt and he said, 'Well, young man, what have you got to say for yourself?'

Well, I wasn't proud of what I'd done, but I wasn't ashamed of it either. As far as I was concerned it was all just a silly misunderstanding, so I said, 'Nothing.'

He went purple. '*Nothing!*' he bellowed. 'You bring shame on this family and you've got nothing to say about it?'

'I haven't brought shame,' I said, sort of half-laughing and trying to make a joke of it. 'I went on the pitch and hugged Geoff Hurst, that was all: I was celebrating. It's not every day England win the World Cup.'

Well, that didn't wash with him at all. He didn't see winning the World Cup as anything special. As far as he was concerned, football was just a lot of silly buggers (not that he would have used that word) running around in shorts and wasting time they could be spending reading the Bible or doing an honest day's work.

I was ostracised, made to feel like a leper. Linda's dad said things like: 'Allowing my daughter to marry a lout like you was the biggest mistake of my life,' and I said things like: 'Yeah, and moving in here with you miserable sods' (that got a gasp of horror from Linda's tight-fannied old stick of a mum) 'was the biggest bloody mistake of *my* life!'

We started really yelling at each other, nine months of clamped-down resentment and frustration and incompatibility and growing mutual dislike all boiling over into one massive great eruption of blistering hatred. In the end, Linda's mum, flapping her hands, squawked, 'Keep it down, think of the neighbours,' and Linda's dad bellowed, 'Oh, sod the neighbours!' and I started laughing because I thought he was finally showing his true colours, and he was so angry that I'd made him lose control like that that he came at me, fists all curled up, a silly old bugger pretending to be a pugilist, and I pushed him down on to the settee (yeah, *settee*, I thought with satisfaction) and he shouted at me, 'Get out, get out of my house now and never come back!'

'Gladly,' I said, and I looked over at Linda, who'd been sitting watching everything with eyes so big they looked as though they might overlap and run into each other. She was a timid soul was Linda, the result of years of being squashed under her parents' thumbs, but unlike them she was kind and open-minded and she liked a laugh now and again as long as it didn't get out of hand.

'Come on, Linda,' I said, 'we're going,' and she just looked at me, not knowing what to do. I think she wanted to come with me, but she was scared of moving because that would have been going against her parents' wishes.

'Linda's going nowhere,' her father said. 'She's staying here with her family. I'm forbidding you to ever see her again.'

'You can't do that, she's my wife,' I pointed out.

'Not any more,' he said. 'The marriage is at an end as from now.'

'I thought divorce was a sin,' I said.

'Being married to a yob like you is an even bigger one,' he answered, and I have to give it to him, he did have a bloody answer for everything.

I tried to get Linda to come with me, but she was too scared to stand up for herself, so in the end I left, pretending it was my decision. At the front door I shouted, 'I only went on the bloody pitch, I didn't murder anybody,' and then I went out, slamming the door behind me.

I went to stay with a friend and work colleague of mine called Barry who thought he was Michael Caine. He dressed like him, acted like him (I don't mean he was an actor, I mean he behaved like him), wore the same kind of glasses and even spoke in the same accent, even though he – Barry, that is – originally came from Birkenhead. When I got to Barry's he was out, celebrating England's win like 99 per cent of the rest of the country, like I should have been doing, so I sat on his doorstep and waited for him to come back. When he did he had a bird on one arm and a crate of Watney's Pale Ale tucked under the other, and he and the bird were weaving all over the street, giggling and snorting and singing bits of football songs. Barry didn't seem surprised to see me. He roared with delight and threw his arms around me and the three of us went inside once Barry had stopped trying to open the door of his flat with the wrong end of his key.

I was feeling a bit melancholy, but I tried to enter into the spirit of things. After a few drinks I was ready to pour my heart out, but every time I tried to impress on Barry and the bird, Janice, that my marriage was over, she just said, 'Aw, poor pet, never mind,' and he said, 'You're best out of there, mate, you mark my words,' and he thrust another beer into my hand.

On the afternoon of the next day, Sunday, I went back to Linda's parents' house, despite what Linda's dad had said to me the night before, to see if I could sort things out. I was determined to be civil, but when I got there all my stuff was in the dustbin on the drive waiting for Monday collection, including my best suit (rumpled), my stamp collection (the album battered and screwed up, the stamps that I'd carefully sorted out all jumbled up with everything else like bits of bloody confetti), and my guitar (the neck broken as if Linda's dad had snapped it over his knee).

I saw red. I kicked at the door until Linda's dad answered, him brandishing that morning's paper with a picture of me hugging Geoff Hurst on the front page, and we ended up first shouting at each other and then having a fist fight on the drive. I punched him on the nose and knocked him down and then I picked up a big flower pot that was sitting by the front door with some geraniums in it and before I could stop myself I threw it through their front window.

By the time the police arrived, some neighbours were pinning me to the front lawn with my hands behind my back, Linda's dad was sitting white-faced against the garage door with blood all over his Sunday suit and Linda herself was sobbing hysterically. I was taken down to the police station for the second time in two days and this time was charged with criminal damage, grievous bodily harm and God knows what else. I was made to fill in some more documents, informed I'd be issued with a date for my second court appearance and was told in no uncertain terms that if I caused any more trouble I'd be thrown into jail until my trial.

I was so upset by what had happened that I went back to Barry's and got horribly, rip-roaringly drunk. Barry had stuck the picture of me hugging Geoff Hurst on the wall of his flat – he didn't admit it, but I knew in his eyes I was now a bit of a celebrity – and I remember staring at it and thinking of how the fortunes of the two men in the photo had contrasted wildly in the twenty-four hours or so since it had been taken. On the one hand there was Geoff Hurst, national hero, the most celebrated and revered man in England, and on the other there was me, whose marriage had collapsed and who was due up in court not just once but twice in the next few weeks.

As I stared at the picture, I wondered what Geoff was doing now – getting happily drunk (as opposed to miserably drunk, like me) on free wine at some celebratory banquet somewhere probably – and as I poured more and more beer down my throat I felt myself growing increasingly bitter. All it would have taken, I thought again, was for Geoff to have nipped over and had a quiet word with the bobby. Thirty seconds of his time, or even less, that was all. Bastard, I thought, selfish bloody bastard. I ripped the picture off the wall and tore it up and threw it in the bin. I wished now that England hadn't won the World Cup, I wished that the Germans had stuffed us.

I was a trainee draughtsman, but I didn't go in to work the next day or for two days after that; I just stayed in and got drunk. Barry covered for me by telling them I had flu, but on the Wednesday night he said, 'I know you've been going through a bad time, old chum, but you'll have to pull yourself together. You can't afford to lose your job on top of everything else.' So the next day I made an effort and went into work with him, and when I got there all the blokes that were mine and Barry's age cheered me and clapped me on the back and asked what Geoff had said to me. They had that bloody picture on the wall, and although it was nice to be treated like something special, I still couldn't look at it without feeling anger and resentment boiling up in my head.

I started work, but I'd only been there ten minutes when word came through that the boss, Mr Drewitt, wanted to see me. I'd been sort of half-expecting it, but my heart sank all the same. Mr Drewitt played golf with Linda's dad which was sort of how I'd got the job in the first place. Linda's dad hadn't been doing me any favours, you understand, he had just wanted to make sure that his daughter would be provided for.

As soon as I walked into his office I knew I was in for it. Drewitt, who had a shiny bald head and a face like an old bulldog, glared at me over the top of his half-moon glasses.

He told me to sit down, and as soon as I'd done that he stood up as though we were playing some silly kids' game.

'Perhaps you'd care to explain to me where you've been these past three days, Mr Jessop,' he said.

Remembering what Barry had told everybody, I said, 'I've had flu, Mr Drewitt. I'm still feeling a bit under the weather now as a matter of fact.'

'I see,' he said, 'so your absence would not have anything to do with the . . . ah . . . incident on Sunday afternoon?'

I thought about playing dumb, pretending I didn't know what he was talking about, but that would only have delayed the inevitable, so I said, 'Not at all, Mr Drewitt.'

'I see,' he said again, then placed his knuckles on the desk and leaned forward. 'Tell me, young man, do you derive pleasure from behaving like a common criminal?'

'No, sir,' I said, shaking my head firmly. 'It was a very regrettable incident and I'm thoroughly ashamed of myself. I'm afraid Linda's dad and I haven't been getting on very well recently, and, well, it all came to a sort of a bit of a head, sir.'

'So your appalling behaviour was just a one-off occurrence, was it, Mr Jessop?' he said.

'Oh yes, sir,' I said, 'very much, sir.'

Of course I should have seen it coming – I bet *you* can, can't you? – but, well, it's different when you're actually there. He opened the top drawer of his desk, produced Sunday's newspaper with *that* picture on the front and slapped it down in front of me.

'Then perhaps you'd care to explain *this*,' he said.

I looked at the picture as though I'd never seen it before as I tried to collect my thoughts. However, my thoughts refused to be collected, and in the end I just said, 'It's Geoff Hurst, sir.'

He closed his eyes briefly, then opened them again. 'I can see that,' he muttered, 'but am I wrong in observing that the lout manhandling him is your good self, Mr Jessop?'

I tried to think of a way out of it, but I couldn't, so a bit flustered I said, 'No, sir. I mean yes, sir, that's me. But I wasn't manhandling him, sir, I was just hugging him. I just got a bit carried away, sir, but I wasn't doing any harm.'

He looked at me for a long moment and then he said, 'Are you telling me that I have received erroneous information, Mr Jessop? I was led to believe that the incident depicted here resulted in your arrest.'

'Er . . . well, yes, sir, it did.'

'And you were arrested again on Sunday, were you not, after the unfortunate events at your father-in-law's home?'

'Yes, sir.'

'Hmmm.' He walked slowly across the room and looked out of the window, his hands clasped behind his back, which meant that I had to twist round to keep him in sight. Addressing himself not to me but to a fly ambling across the window pane, he said, 'You do appreciate, Mr Jessop, that the good name of this company must be upheld at all times?'

'What good name?' I almost said, but I didn't, I said, 'Of course, sir.'

'And I am sure you also therefore appreciate that any employee who, by his actions, threatens to sully that good name must be dealt with in the severest possible terms?'

Well, what did he expect me to say to that? 'Yes, I quite agree, sir. I deserve to be horse-whipped, sir'? I kept my mouth shut.

He looked at me sharply. 'Have you nothing to say, Mr Jessop?'

Oh yes, I had plenty to say. I felt the bitterness rising up in me again, but I managed to keep my voice quite calm as I asked him, 'Are you going to sack me?'

He seemed taken aback and a bit annoyed by the directness of my question. Obviously his plan had been to get shot of me in a roundabout way with me apologising profusely for putting him in such a difficult situation and sympathetically agreeing that he simply had no alternative.

He bumbled, 'Well . . . ah, regretfully, Mr Jessop, you must appreciate –'

'Linda's dad has told you to get rid of me, hasn't he?' I cut in.

He went red with either embarrassment or indignation, or maybe both. 'Certainly not,' he blustered. 'This has been a con-sidered company decision based on –'

'Bollocks,' I said. 'He rang you up and said that if you didn't get rid of me he wouldn't play golf with you any more. And I bet you need all the friends you can get, don't you, Mr Drewitt, seeing as how your breath smells like an elephant's arse?'

So there you go. In less than a week I'd lost my wife and my job (not to mention my guitar and stamp collection), I had nowhere to live and once my court cases came up I'd probably end up getting chucked into prison. Given those circumstances and my less than rational state of mind I decided to follow what I considered at the time to be the only reasonable course of action left open to me.

I was going to kill Geoff Hurst.

Yes, yes, I know. With hindsight that decision seems utterly ludicrous even to me, but what I feel I have to keep emphasising is that back then my mind was not functioning normally. I mean on the outside I seemed fairly okay, if naturally a bit pissed off by all that had happened (just ask Barry, he'll tell you), but – and this is hard to explain – on the inside I just couldn't make sense of things. To the inner me, my outer persona seemed like a shell, a disguise that I was hiding my true self behind. I suppose I was having some sort of mental breakdown – well, I *know* I was, the doctor told me – but at the time all the weird thoughts I was having, all the strange, skewed connections that my mind was making seemed logical and sensible.

I don't know whether I thought that killing Geoff Hurst would make everything all right again or whether I just wanted revenge; as I say, my brain wasn't really functioning in such conventional terms. All I know is that whenever I looked at the ruin that my life had rapidly become, all the tangled routes seemed to lead back to Geoff, which as far as I was concerned meant there could be only one possible conclusion.

I found it ridiculously easy to get a gun. There was this bloke Barry knew who was a bit of a gangster, and he told me to be at this pub called The Three Tuns in East London at seven o'clock the following Tuesday evening, where I was to meet a bloke called Bernie. The gun, he said, would cost me a hundred and fifty pounds and Bernie would want the money in used tenners.

Well, as I've said before, Linda and I had been saving up for a house and I had a bit in the bank, so I withdrew the money and the next Tuesday evening went to the pub. As soon as I walked in this weaselly little bloke came up to me and said, 'What you drinking, Mr Jessop?' and I said, 'Are you Bernie?' and he said, 'Yes,' and I said, 'I've got the money,' and he sort of grimaced, showing me all these dark brown, broken teeth, and looked around and hissed, 'Keep your bleedin' voice down, pal. Do you want your throat cut?'

Well, we had a drink together and he said, 'You're that bloke what hugged Geoff Hurst, aren't you?' and I said, 'Yes,' and he said, 'What was he like then, up close?' and I said, 'Sweaty.' Then we went out to the car park and got into his car, a rusty old Austin Seven, and he started the engine and we went for a drive.

I don't really know where we drove to, I wasn't paying that much attention. We just went up and down a lot of streets and under the occasional railway bridge, passing houses and shops and schools and factories.

'Open the glove compartment, take out the plastic bag inside and put it in your pocket and put the money where the bag was,' he said, so I did. We drove a bit further in silence and then he said, 'He's a bloody hero, that Geoff Hurst. I wish I'd done what you did. You must be dead proud of yourself. It's something to tell your grandchildren about, isn't it? What do you want the gun for, by the way, if you don't mind me asking?'

'I'm going to shoot my father-in-law,' I said without hesitation.

He nodded. 'Good luck to you, mate. I hope you get away with it.'

England won the World Cup in July 1966 – well, we all know that, don't we? – but what this meant was I couldn't kill Geoff Hurst right away. I had to wait a few weeks for the new season to start, and I spent most of the intervening time thinking about my plan, polishing my gun, sitting around getting drunk and going more and more mad – or should that be madder and madder?

Anyway, I let myself go a bit, not only in the brain department, but in the hygiene department too. Barry had a go at me about it, but he couldn't get through to me. He said I was cramping his style and that if I didn't sort myself out I'd have to go, because after all there were plenty more jobs out there and plenty more birds to poke, but my only response was to shut myself away in the bathroom for hours at a time, where I'd sit rocking backwards and forwards on the bog, and in the end he gave up (to be honest, I think he was a bit scared of me, and with bloody good reason, it has to be said).

The day finally came: West Ham's first home match of the season. I was so focused on what I was going to do, so determined to get it right, that I didn't even know who the opposition were. I can't really remember now as a matter of fact, though I've a feeling it might have been one of the Lancashire clubs: Blackburn Rovers or Preston North End. Then again it might have been Tottenham. Or Everton. Or was it Derby?

Anyway, to Barry's delight I got myself spruced up for the first time in ages. By the time I'd had a bath and put on clean clothes I looked just like any other normal person. When Barry asked me where I was going and I said Upton Park, his face lit up.

'I'll come with you,' he said. 'Then afterwards we could go for a pie and a few pints and then down the Mitre to pull a couple of birds. What do you say?'

'I'm going on my own,' I said, and there must have been something in my face or my voice, something cold and weird, because I distinctly remember his face falling and him backing off as if I'd taken out the gun that I'd tucked down the front of my trousers and pointed it at his head.

'All right,' he mumbled, 'if that's how you feel.'

'It is,' I said, and I walked out of his flat and I haven't seen him since.

I remember, as I got near Upton Park, the swell of the crowd sort of buoying me up, carrying me along, as if I was a boat on a rolling ocean. It seemed to me back then as though the atmosphere of that day had a kind of grandeur to it; it was almost a divine feeling, as if far above me in the heavens planets were shifting, tilting, realigning themselves, creating the perfect circumstances for my plan to be carried out.

There was an optimism in the air that afternoon, a freshness and a clarity that came not just from the fact that it was a nice day and the start of a new season, but also from the knowledge that England were now officially the best footballing nation in the world. Here on these sparkling green pitches enclosed within these shabby stadia, between these crumbling terraces and scratching sheds with their rusty corrugated iron roofs, the cream of the entire planet's footballing population practised their scintillating art.

And here, at Upton Park, was the Godhead, the greatest footballing hero of them all. I didn't want to gain anything out of Geoff Hurst's death except maybe, in some skewed way, a sense of inner peace, but I can't deny that somewhere in my twisted maelstrom of a mind was a bubble of thought, a notion that by killing Geoff Hurst I would somehow be setting myself up above the Gods.

Ironically, even though just a few weeks before, I'd clapped him on his sweaty back, I didn't think of Geoff Hurst as a living, breathing, thinking, feeling person any more. I didn't think of his family, of the people who loved him and who would be devastated by his death. I didn't think of any of that. I just thought of him as a symbol, an evil talisman, if you like, which I had touched and which as a consequence had brought about my downfall and which I now had to get rid of.

Or did I? To be honest, I can't really remember exactly what I was thinking. Like I say, I was a different person back then. It now seems that big parts of my mind were just holes full of confusing nonsense that I'm now trying to plug with what feels like an approximation of the truth.

I paid my money and went in and took my place. I remember thinking about Lee Harvey Oswald, the assassin finding his place and settling himself down and waiting for his moment. I had no doubt that my moment would come and when it did I would know. I didn't know exactly when that would be, but I didn't feel anxious about it. In fact, I felt very calm, very centred.

The teams came on and they got a fantastic reception and they kicked about a bit and then the game started. As the action ebbed and flowed on the pitch, the crowd surged like iron filings attracted to the pull of a magnet. People were getting buffeted this way and that, but I felt oblivious to it all, felt as though it was happening around me, but not *to* me, felt like an immovable rock in a stormy sea.

I didn't see the game. I didn't see goals and throw-ins and corners and tackles; I was focusing solely on my chosen target. Geoff and I were umbilically linked; we were like twins.

He seemed to glow. He was an angel. For a while he capered teasingly out of my range and then suddenly he seemed to accept his fate and he just walked meekly over and stood there, waiting for the magic bullet. I suppose, with hindsight, what happened was this: it was the first half and West Ham were kicking towards the goal behind which I was standing. They got a corner and Geoff Hurst came up and stood on the penalty spot, waiting for someone to take it.

I knew it was my moment. Everything melted away around me as, in one fluid, almost balletic movement, I pulled out the gun, pointed it and fired. Nothing happened and I fired again. Geoff fell over. I was about to fire again when reality suddenly roared in at me. I heard incredible noise and felt hard blocks of pain smashing into my body from all sides. I went down under a flurry of boots and fists. My wrist broke as someone stamped on it and the gun fell out of my hand and everything went black.

I've seen the news footage of the incident since and it's not how I remember it at all.

It seems so . . . mundane somehow, so rooted in hard, nasty reality. The players are standing around waiting for the corner to be taken when there's a bang and they all look round, into the crowd. They don't look scared, just surprised. None of them really realise what's going on. Then there's another bang and Geoff Hurst crumples to the ground. His body's heaving and arching and he's clutching his left thigh with both hands and his knee's just a mass of . . . well, it would have been red if it had been in colour, but it's just black on the set in the TV room. There's that famous bit of commentary that everyone knows by heart now, Kenneth Wolstenholme saying, 'I think Hurst has been shot. Some people are on the pitch. They're tending to him now, but it doesn't look good.'

It wasn't good, as we all know. Geoff didn't die, but his knee and part of his thigh bone were shattered. He'll never play football again and he'll spend the rest of his days walking with a limp. As for me, some people think I came out of the pummelling I took pretty lightly. My wrist and four of my ribs were broken and I got a hairline fracture of the skull and lots of cuts and bruises.

I've written to Geoff apologising for what I did, but he hasn't written back. A lot of people won't ever forgive me and I don't blame them; what I did *was* unforgivable. I'm not looking for sympathy, I just wanted to set the record straight, to answer the questions that people are asking about why I did it, and hopefully to some extent I've done that now. I know my words will sound hollow to a lot of people, but I just wanted everyone to know that I wish Geoff all the best for the future. I really do.

THE ECSTASY

England's Shame

Geoff Nicholson

Welcome to The Legless Winger, London's latest, most stylish football theme pub. I'm your genial landlord Ray Swan, and this is my domain. Check out the decor, the interactive displays of football memorabilia; scratch-and-sniff football shirts, signed balls, preserved half-time oranges that have been sucked by some of the biggest stars in the game. In the loo you'll find a condom machine that dispenses johnnies in team colours. It's all good stuff. But sooner or later all eyes fall on the framed newspaper page above the bar and the headline that reads 'ENGLAND'S SHAME'.

Well, nothing new there you might say. Over the years shame is one of those things the English national soccer team has become pretty well used to dealing with. The difference with this headline, this particular shame, is that it arrived the morning after we'd won the 2010 World Cup finals in Tangier, a match in which I bagged the winning goal. I'll see if I can explain.

As a matter of fact there were those who said the entire 2010 competition was shameful from beginning to end, but I couldn't really agree with that. It all seemed inevitable to me. All through the 1980s and 1990s and for the first decade of the new millennium people had tried to clean up international football, to make it drug free. War had been declared on artificial stimulants. There had been random sampling of blood, urine and semen, before, after and even during the game, but I think the authorities knew they were on a hiding to nothing. The truth was that the modern footballer is the kind of guy who wants edge. He wants to give himself every possible advantage. He wants the latest gear, the latest tactics, the latest metabolic enhancements.

Also he likes to party, likes to get high, likes to mess about with the boundaries of consciousness. How could a few old football legislators and bureaucratic fogies possibly combat that sort of thing? They couldn't and they knew it.

So when they were drawing up the rules for the 2010 finals, some bright spark at FIFA said, 'All right, enough's enough. Sod it, if we can't effectively legislate against drugs, then why bother? Let the buggers take all the drugs they want and see how they like it. It'll certainly make our lives a lot easier.'

So, for these finals they decreed that anything and everything was acceptable. May the best team, with the best players, the best drugs and best drug dealers, win. It was a simple idea but a brilliant one. And Tangier, with its reputation for free trade, and its *laissez-faire* attitude towards getting wasted, was obviously the best place for the World Cup. In fact it was just about the only place, since nobody else actually wanted to host a competition involving teams of highly trained, highly committed drug abusers.

There were those who said the whole thing would never work, but these were the same killjoys who said it was ludicrous to have Cilla Black singing 'Waiting For The Man' as the official World Cup Song. OK, so it didn't sound like an obvious hit, but in the event it topped the charts for six weeks.

Now, personally I've always been a rather old-fashioned sort of footballer. I've never been much of a one for fancy drugs that you had to snort or inhale or inject. Alcohol's always been my favourite mood-enhancer. Call me an old fart if you like.

I'd had an up and down season prior to the World Cup. I'd been in and out of the international team. I'd had my moments of brilliance, but also moments of comparative plonkerdom. I'd scored some blinders but missed some sitters.

I knew I wasn't a dead certainty for the World Cup squad, but I hoped I was still in with a chance. I reckoned it was all down to what drug strategy the team decided to adopt. But when I heard that the boss was taking an ultra-traditionalist stance I thought things were looking much better for me, and when I heard the English team had got a sponsorship deal with Wetley's Pennine Bitter, I knew I was on my way to Tangier.

Some people carped of course. They said beer was a backwards-looking choice, that we should be using something a bit more state of the art, a bit more designerish, but I reckoned the boss knew what he was doing. Heritage is what we English have always been best at.

Other sides had more difficulty. All around the world managers and coaches had to completely rethink the way they played the game and, of course, they had to select the substance that was going to work best with their players' temperaments and constitutions.

Some choices were easy. The Bolivians obviously went for Bolivian marching powder. The Dutch went for hash. The Scots went for industrial solvents. But there were other, more surprising choices. Who will ever know why Norway plumped for amyl nitrate? Or why Wales chose horse tranquillizer? But I suppose that's how it is with drugs; things get irrational.

We got into training early, practising ball skills, analyzing videos, getting tanked on barrels of Wetley's. It was a demanding programme, but we stuck to it. We grew in confidence. We let go of our inhibitions. We had an exaggerated sense of our self worth.

We were in a tough preliminary group. I thought we had most to fear from the Germans who'd decided to go the steroid route. They were big strapping lads, fearless, pumped up, but they were an impatient, muscle-bound bunch, given to terrible bouts of roid rage. When things weren't going their way they'd attack opposing players, the referee, linesmen, each other, and when one of them beat up a harmless old programme seller, threatening to pull his arms off and urinate in the stumps, well I think we all knew they weren't going to go all the way. And frankly they weren't that difficult to play against. In any game a good five or six of them were guaranteed to get sent off. We played silky, well-oiled football against them and won 2-0, and although we got a few bruised shins and black eyes, we were pretty happy. But then most of the teams were happy at this stage, and one or two were positively ecstatic.

Also in the group were the USA, nicknamed the Prozac Nation, and Portugal who were using multiple nicotine patches stuck to each arm; they were stimulated all right, but they had a bit of trouble concentrating. We won the group without too much bother.

News came in from the other groups. The Italian side were strongly fancied. They'd begun by claiming that religion was their drug, the opium of the people and all that, but the authorities said religion was just a placebo and so the Italians consumed heroic quantities of sambuca. They were playing well, but it sounded like a ladies' drink to me.

One of the more inventive drug strategies came from the Peruvians who went for yagi, the mystical, controversial, but wholly organic compound that allegedly creates telepathic effects between users. Mind-reading was obviously extremely handy when it came to the dummy, free kicks and unexpected back passes, but it wasn't so good when the players looked into each other's minds and realized what contempt they all had for each other. And when one of their forwards read the mind of the manager and discovered he was having dirty thoughts about the forward's wife, there was pandemonium.

Of course, there's always one team in every competition, some lowly underdog that plays above itself and wins the hearts and minds of the public, and this year it was the Mauritanians. They didn't have much in the way of training facilities. When they arrived at the finals the only drug they could afford was some non-prescription cough mixture. Fortunately a major pharmaceutical company stepped in and supplied them with a state-of-the-art, still experimental drug that claimed to cure alimentary canal parasites. It certainly created some colourful on-field side effects, although improved ball skills, alas, was not one of them.

By the time of the quarter-finals some teams were feeling the strain. Players were starting to experience toxic reactions of greater or lesser severity, and one or two were displaying alarming personality disorders. Various players complained of tachycardia, hypertension, sleeplessness. There was moodiness, dizziness, slurred speech and emotional lability, though it was agreed that these things were not entirely unknown to the modern footballer. In the England camp we had the usual aches and pains, the usual niggling injuries, but for most of the time the lads were feeling no pain at all.

We played against Morocco, the home team, drug of choice heroin, and frankly it was a bit of a walk-over. In a touching if unintentional homage to William Burroughs most of the Moroccans spent the entire ninety minutes staring at their boots or going on the nod, though they did look elegantly wasted, I had to admit. I hate to blow my own trumpet but I played some very cultured football and hammered home a couple of pretty good goals.

And so to the semi-final. It was against Spain, and frankly I never thought they were going to be much of a threat. They, bloody fools that they were, got drugged up on Spanish fly. It was obvious to me that getting loaded on an aphrodisiac was never going to get the job done, especially since the back four kept leaving the field for a quicky. We thrashed them, and they looked very dispirited, although apparently the scenes in their showers after the match were something to behold.

And then the final. We were just ninety minutes away from glory and all we had to do was beat the Brazilians, drug of choice LSD, no I don't know why either. I thought they'd have been better off with caffeine.

It was not a classic final. We gave a scrappy performance; too many passes went astray, too many chances were wasted. You could put it down to the inevitable nerves caused by the big occasion but I'd be more inclined to put it down to hangovers, shakes, lack of motor coordination and the occasional black-out. But we still had the measure of the Brazilians.

Putting your faith in a major psychedelic was a high-risk strategy if ever there was one. A heightened awareness of colour, movement and space was all very well, but along with it came the tendency to become engrossed in things like the movement of the clouds, or the way the light reflected off the goalposts, or a desire on the part of their midfield to get naked, roll on the turf and become one with the cosmos.

Still, it was a tight game, and we couldn't find our rhythm, or the net, or in the case of some players, even the corner flag. It was a long frustrating game, and with only a couple of minutes of the match remaining, the score line was still nil-nil.

And that was when one of our lads was brought down by their goalkeeper. Our man didn't know much about the incident and the goalkeeper knew even less since he was having a nasty flashback at the time and was re-experiencing his time in the womb.

We were awarded a penalty. There was a bit of debate about who was going to take it, and then a number of drunken threats and offers to step outside and settle the argument like a man. But I got the job, and even though it was a nerve-racking moment I slipped the ball home cool as a cucumber. The fact that their keeper was by that time having a severe bad trip and ran away from his line thinking the ball was a small vicious animal coming to tear his throat out, was neither here nor there. The goal had scarcely been scored when the final whistle went and we were glorious winners.

I was lifted shoulder high by the rest of the team. They dropped me, of course. And then they all said they wanted to go off and have a curry, and stuff the medal ceremony, but it was only the drink talking.

I naturally assumed I was going to be a national hero, but the accusations and rumours about me started almost immediately.

The cool way I'd slotted home the ball, the way I was balanced and steady on my feet, the way my eyes stayed focused; I hardly seemed pissed at all.

The fans and the commentators, and in fact several members of my own team, jumped to the immediate conclusion that I was a cheat, and what was worse, that I was sober. Of course, the English camp didn't really mind the cheating per se, they reckoned it was just 'gamesmanship'. But as it dawned on them that I must have been knocking back the non-alcoholic lager while the rest of the lads had been doing all the serious hard drinking, their attitude changed.

I tried to say I had an iron constitution, that I could hold my drink, but nobody was having any of it. They did a blood test on me. It was terrible; there was a bit of alcohol but not much. Not enough to impress. It would even have been legal for me to drive.

I was vilified twice over. The foreign press called me a scoundrel, a fake, a crook. Oh, maybe I hadn't broken any rules, but I'd been totally unsporting. I'd offended against the entire spirit of the game. I'd been drinking, but I hadn't been drinking enough. Where was my sense of fair play? Why hadn't I got totally out of it and incoherent like everybody else?

The English reaction was different. Cheating they could cope with, but a bloke who bottled out when it came to getting plastered, that was unacceptable. Why had I been so un-English, such a wimp, such a pantywaist? Why had I wanted to bring about England's shame?

And the answer, naturally, is that I hadn't wanted to at all. I'd wanted to do an honest job for the lads and the boss, but after all those weeks of training I'd come to the conclusion that Wetley's Pennine Bitter was bloody awful stuff, and it was weak as gnat's piss in any case. I didn't mind forcing down a couple of pints for the sake of morale and to show willing, but no way could I drink enough of it to get properly pissed. It was enough to put you off drink altogether, and in fact it had. I'd been pouring pints away when nobody was looking.

From reading the papers you'd have thought I was the Anti-Christ, although in fact one of them called me the Anti-George Best. I was reviled, denounced, mocked. I knew it was all over, that my career was ruined. I'd imagined I'd find myself rocketed to international stardom, spend a few years in Italian football then come back to England to be a television pundit. As things stood, I was offered a free transfer but nobody would take me on, and I found myself looking for a job outside of football.

So that's when I decided to go into pub management and eventually found myself running this place, The Legless Winger. It's not such a bad life, and it's something that lots of ex-players would be happy to spend their days doing, but I must say I'd been hoping for more out of life.

Anyway, no point brooding about it. Come in, sit down, relax, join me in a drink. What's your poison? Mine's a triple brandy. The doctors have told me I'm drinking too much, but what do they know? We'll soon have you legless, like me, though if you really want to get pissed, I do suggest you give a wide berth to the Wetley's Pennine Bitter.

1-1-1

Conrad Williams

My first experience of football came at Goodison Park in 1976. Dad was an Everton fan and, in the futile attempts all dads make when confronted with sons and football, he tried to introduce me to his team, to the silky skills of Latchford and Rioch. Dai Davies was in goal. We took a flask and some sandwiches for half time. I must have grown bored because I spent much of the second half tossing the acorns I had stashed in my pocket on to the heads of supporters standing below me. We stayed until ten minutes before time, Everton one up against Derby. Dad decided we should get going and headed back to the car. A roar went up outside the ground, obviously from the Everton supporters. It was cold. Late afternoon. Dark. And Kevin Keegan wasn't playing. Fatal mistake.

I had fallen for Kevin Keegan in a bad way, me and thousands of other kids, but when football is concerned you don't realise who else is involved. Kevin played for me. Nobody else. He played for Liverpool, yes, but he played for me first. No doubt to my dad's chagrin (although to his credit he never said anything about it, apart from later chiding me about how useless Liverpool are now) I became a Liverpool supporter. Dad was great about it. Within the first season of my following them, he had taken me to see them whup WBA 3-1 at home. I knew the team inside out and all of them were my favourites. In particular, because I fancied myself as a goalkeeper then (I was pretty good too, although these days I couldn't catch a cliché), I had a bit of a crush on Ray Clemence. One of the first Anfield matches Dad took me to, at half time I watched my players troop off the pitch and I put a thumb up to Ray, who smiled and waved back. How could I support anybody else after that? How could I support anybody else after Scum Utd (sorry, Man Utd, but you understand) beat the Mighty Reds 2-1 in the 1977 FA cup final. The die was cast. I loved my team unconditionally. I hated Man U, just like everyone else. That's football. We won the European Cup – me and Mum sitting on the PVC sofa on a rainy May night while the lads stuck it to Borussia Mönchengladbach in Rome. Us screaming and laughing and hugging each other. Just twelve years after we'd stuck it to the Germans in an entirely different way in a competition I didn't understand or even know about. I had cried for my team. For me, football was Liverpool winning the league, losing the FA Cup and doing something noisy and exciting in Europe against a team I could barely pronounce. The idea of England as a football team didn't exist for me. Not then. And the apogee of footballing excellence happened in a concrete playground just fifty yards away from my house at Bewsey Junior School. Me, Jeff Wilcocks and Carl Weston against everyone else. The ball at my feet, I could truly understand the thrill of the beautiful game and why it ripped my insides out. I'd come home in the evenings and Dad would take me into the garden with a ball and blast fizzing shots for me to save. He had been a professional footballer for Witton Albion and Stockport in the 1950s – a goalkeeper – and I was eager to please. He told me that the only time his dad, my grandfather, went to watch him play, he had saved a penalty. He didn't have to go into it then and I don't have to go into it now. You know what that meant.

A year later and I was Graeme Souness. Wezzy was Kenny Dalglish and Jeff was Alan Hansen. Three English lads posing as Scotsmen. Liverpool defended their European Cup win and then, as was the case after May, there was no football. Except, there was . . . this business of Argentina, a place I didn't know about but which possessed such bewitching names. Cordoba, Mendoza, Rosario. The River Plate Stadium.

It didn't matter that we hadn't qualified. How could it matter? I was eight years old. I didn't know what qualifying meant. It was a World Cup. It was my first World Cup. I was entranced. Teams I never knew existed were playing each other for the most important prize on the planet. I felt as though the teams that couldn't land the trophy were damned to an eternity of pain, so damaged did they look when they let in a goal. World Cup. A new type of soccer to take my affinity for the game to a rarefied plateau. Before June 1978, when all I knew about football was muddy winter battles and my red-shirted heroes, the World Cup might as well have been called the Warrington Beaker for all it meant to me. But here we were. Football in the sun. Exotically named (and exotically maned) athletes.

Wezzy was a brilliant football player, a short, stocky, ginger-haired dynamo who had a demon sprint on him and tucked balls away between our makeshift posts (duffel coats, satchels . . . on one memorable occasion Jason Bebbington) with the aplomb of an Ian Rush. Jeff was a solid defender. A thickset Phil Thompson who could collect the ball deep before it became a danger and nurse it out of the back lines, looking for me or Wezzy to make the killer run. Me, I was a left winger, that was it. I'd like to think I was capable of amazing skill and incredible foresight, but maybe I was just quick and hard to tackle. No defender likes a fast winger bearing down on them. Me, in my NHS specs fastened together at the corners with Elastoplast. Me, in my comfy Clarks and flared 'slacks', trying to be Steve Heighway, trying to win the European Cup single-handedly.

Football in the playground had its hazards. Sometimes girls played football in aberrant sessions, usually when some skirt-chasing toddler had brought the only ball in and wouldn't let us play unless the girls could get involved too. The only thing sadder than watching a girl who can't play kick a football is watching one attempt to throw a ball. Or run.

Back then, we didn't know what Reeboks or Nikes were and even if we had done, we wouldn't have been allowed to wear them to school. We wore clod-hopping shoes 'for comfort' and these were our Adidas Predators. Coming home to a rollicking for getting your shoes scuffed was worth it if you'd managed to replicate some piece of magic by Kenny, or Frank Worthington or Liam Brady, in the playground. Brady, Heighway, Peter Barnes and – I hate to say it – Steve Coppell, were my role models. Forward wingers were fashionable then, not the attacking defenders you find playing these days. Nobody had the engine for that kind of malarkey in the seventies, except maybe Alan 'running himself daft' Ball, but he was just before my time. In the eighties, in England terms I would have proved Peter Beardsley to Wezzy's Gary Lineker; in the nineties, Sheringham to his Shearer. Back then, I provided Wezzy with the ammo; he fired the shells. I scored too, usually with long-range efforts with my sweet left foot (could have opened a tin can with it). But our prosaic efforts were to be rendered utterly graceless by the things we saw on TV, late every night, parents permitting, from Argentina as the World Cup kicked off.

England had failed to qualify by the slimmest margin, finishing their group runners-up to Italy on goal difference (there wasn't the safety net of a play-off against Russia in those days . . .). It didn't matter though, for as the competition drew on, there were players we had never heard of who were doing things on a football pitch that we'd never seen before. We witnessed in such players as Paolo Rossi (who would come into his own four years later in Spain) and Roberto Bettega for Italy, Johnny Rep and Arie Haan for Holland, Kempes and Luque for Argentina, the subtleties of the game where previously we had known only the English 'virtues' of grit, guts and gung-hoism. Arie Haan scored two goals that had my eyes on stalks, long-range efforts between 30 and 35 yards against West Germany and Italy during the second phase of group matches; Rossi and Bettega played off each other with bewildering telepathy; in Luque and Kempes, Argentina boasted an attacking force that proved impossible to contain. It was only years later that the scandals of that World Cup (name one in its 68-year history that hasn't produced some moment of controversy) dawned on me.

As a nine-year-old, the footballing problems that bother you are minuscule: how to get past the tenacious defending of Brian Bedford; how to avoid the game getting snarled up with the girls playing netball; how to attract the attention of the surly old giffer across the road to get him to throw the ball back. I wasn't aware of the military dictatorship and the thousands that had disappeared since the junta took control two years before; I wasn't even aware of the less global but equally newsworthy items: the abject refereeing, the death of Luque's brother before the final (he burned to death in a car accident), the strong suspicion that Argentina's rout of Peru (needing to win by at least four goals lest Brazil go to the final – they scored six) was fixed. Bizarrely, the one scandalous image that stays with me is Tony Gubba, filmed at night, pate incandescent under the spotlights as he told of Scotland's Willie Miller, the random dope test that found he had been taking 'pep' pills. In Gubba's hand were a few samples, liquefying under the heat of the spots.

In the playground we attempted to emulate Archie Gemmill's mazy run through the defence for Scotland in their 3-2 win over the Dutch. We played audacious one-twos, we threw ourselves between duffel coat goalposts, midget Zoffs and Maiers.

The whistle blew and we froze, as we were ordered to do so by the staff. The next blast was the order for the girls to file inside. Once they were gone, a third whistle was our cue. Crushed by the abortion of our game we'd troop indoors, certain that, with another few minutes, we could have got the goals to secure our triple hat-tricks. In the classrooms, sweating like herded animals, we'd pore over Beta books, thinking of the tournament half a world away. What was the point of adding fractions when, in six years' time, I could be creaming defences with my runs down the wing while the Kop surged in awed, immanent silence.

'What do you want to be when you grow up?' I whispered at Wezzy, sitting on the next table.

'Painter and decorator,' he said. 'And then I'd like to go abroad and play for someone like Ajax.'

Our paths would surely cross in the future, when Liverpool drew the Dutch team in some European competition or other. Eschewing the finer points of primary school mathematics, I played the encounter out in my head. European Cup Final. Two-all at the fag-end of extra time. Wezzy and I had played each other to a standstill. He had scored two supreme poacher's goals, simple tap-ins that highlighted the anticipatory nature of his play. I had responded twice, once a snaking run from half way that ended with a left-foot shot that all but ripped out the back of the net; the second a sweet volley from forty yards that had our supporters screaming in ecstasy. The referee looking at his watch. Liverpool break and I get the ball at my feet on the left wing. A buzz goes around the stadium. A hundred flares as a hundred cameras catch my image at the moment of my burst for goal. A look up: only Wezzy in my way. He's expecting me to try to dance past him so I just knock the ball and run. We both sprint for it, me needing that half-yard from his surprise. The goalkeeper advancing, I sense the ref with the whistle at his lips. Wezzy's breath blasts against me as he makes his challenge. A window appears, very small, but it's all I need.

Impact.

Hit with the outside of my left boot, the ball swerves past the goalkeeper into the top right-hand corner. The stadium erupts. I can almost hear John Motson emote: 'It's there!'

And out of the scrum of red shirts on the terraces as the ref blows for the end of the game:

'One Connie Williams, there's only one Connie Williams . . .'

Wezzy and me looking at each other with respect and affection, perhaps nodding at each other, swapping shirts and looking up to the stand where we can read the lips of England boss Ron Greenwood saying to his assistants: 'I want those two boys spearheading our World Cup campaign.'

The crowd: 'Connie's here, Connie's there, Connie's every-fucking-where . . .'

'Conradulations and celebrations . . .'

'Conrad? Conrad? What's the score? Conrad? What's *a half times a quarter? Pay attention boy!'*

If only the epic encounters in our heads and those played out against lesser mortals on the concrete playground could have been replicated on the grass pitches of Warrington's schools. I don't know why they weren't. Perhaps it was because our games teacher, Mr Rees, didn't have a clue. When he played soccer he toe-poked the ball. I reckon he was told to do the job, being relatively new to the school and certainly the youngest member of staff. He didn't give us any training or attempt to improve our skills. He simply handed out coloured bibs and told us to get on with it, while he sipped from a flask and nibbled one of Mr Kipling's individual fruit pies.

There were some decent players on our team. What Andrew Hilditch lacked in skill, he made up for in enthusiasm. Ian Warburton was a wiry right winger who could drift past players as though they weren't there. Weldon Cheek was an excellent tackler, even though he moved like a duck stricken with haemorrhoids.

We were all eager to do well but there wasn't really any rhythm or penetration there. Mr Rees, the master tactician, dropped his plan on us before the games: 'Give it to Wezzy,' he said. Wez, natural striker that he was, scored plenty, but we let in more. One game against Brookacre saw us reach our footballing nadir. We were bollocked 13-2.

Mum and Dad let me stay up late to watch the World Cup final. I wasn't concerned with all the arguments, all that empty punditry. Argentina shouldn't really be in the final; Holland, without Cruyff not having the cutting edge to turn them into serious contenders to be the first European team to win the World Cup in South America . . . The spectacle, viewed on our ageing Philips, sucked the breath from me. As the cameras panned in on the River Plate Stadium, I thought the TV had given up the ghost, picture destroyed by an attack of white noise. But no, it was confetti. Hundreds of thousands of fragments of paper whipping above the pitch. Ask me for my most enduring, positive vision of football and I will point you towards that moment, the teams trooping on to the pitch beneath a maelstrom. It bit deep into me and suddenly it *did* matter that England hadn't qualified. I was entranced by the match, although I remember very little about it now, other than it went into extra time and Argentina rallied to triumph 3-1 over the World Cup bridesmaids of the '70s. Kempes, the tournament's top scorer bagging a brace, his long black hair flaring behind him as he closed in on goal. Argentina might not have been worthy winners that year, but Mario Kempes deserved his medal.

A year or so later and we're in the big school. Uniforms. Jeff, Wezzy and me are separated into different streams. We make new friends. There are other boys from the district's feeder schools who fill in the gaps between our talents and the other boys we knew. Like members in a strong footballing unit who mature together and grow too old for the team, we eventually fell apart, still playing in the school set-up but no longer with that special bond that we had known. We were very close, me and Wez, and anyone who remembers what having a best friend at school was really like will know how deep those friendships go, how much they matter, regardless of their ephemeral nature. We were joined by our love of football. God, he even kissed my girlfriend, ten years before I went out with her.

Even now I can see him in the hooped green and white of Bewsey's kit, bearing down on goal, his red hair like a beacon in the cold of a winter Saturday. This and the remembered sounds of studs on concrete, of wintergreen and musty changing rooms gives me an ache that is close to grief but warmed by the happiness that at least I had been involved. Those non-footballers, those geeks poring over their Top Trumps or playing kiss-chase with the girls – I hope you're reading this. You missed out.

There have been plenty of footballing triumphs for me since then, lots of agony too. At the time of writing, Liverpool are licking their wounds having gone down 3-1 against Scum at Anfield for the second time this year. Jesus *wept*. But 1978 was my baptism, the World Cup and the beginning of my own modest career as a casual player. I played in an under 15s match against Wezzy once, my dream in miniature – when I was a left-winger for Penlake and he a right-winger for Rope & Anchor. I scored that day, and I believe he did too, but we never tussled because our routes of attack never crossed. It was a season in which I scored my first goal in front of Dad, who used to run me to the matches on Sundays. I can remember turning away from goal, having chipped the keeper as he came to collect from my feet and seeing Dad at the touchline, wrapped in his big sheepskin. 'Good goal, Con,' he called. I didn't acknowledge him, because, well, you don't. But it's a memory I'll take to the grave. Football – it does things for you like that. It hands out some fantastic treats.

These days I still see Wezzy, now and again. We nod, say hello, virtual strangers. But walking on, I can't help but believe that he too has been caught up by the ropes reaching out through time, dragging us back to a day when we found our religion in a playground where we had clicked with each other, firing the short future of our connection with a glory that has never been equalled.

Hysterical Men

Rosie Jackson

It was my fault Angel lost her finger.

We were scaling the inner security fence at Glastonbury festival, speeding and reckless at having so easily clambered over the outer wall. Not that this had much to do with agility – someone had kindly left a step-ladder dangling over the eight-foot-high reinforced steel. And at the inner barrier, with its equally tall screen of vicious wire mesh, our luck deserted us. One of the protruding spikes hooked itself through Angel's serpent ring, and as she dropped the last few feet towards dank black grass – it was the middle of the night – her finger shot off in the opposite direction, catapulted into noisy darkness.

Clever women are adept at making men feel guilty, and Angel's no exception. But this time, I just couldn't shrug off blame. As Angel indignantly pointed out, if I'd not been so suspicious of where the festival profits actually went, not been so cynical of all that fig-leaf Greenpeace charity, I'd simply have splashed out and paid for tickets. She waved her hand in my face as she spoke, as if the lost finger symbolised something, as if it confirmed the worst male sins.

Naturally, after that I was easy prey. For the next two weeks, I was a perfect new man. I shopped, cooked, did the housework, scrubbed the loo. I stopped furtively scanning newspaper head-lines to check progress in the World Cup. I dropped the plot I'd been secretly hatching to find somewhere to watch the final. (Angel doesn't approve of TV.)

Worse than all that, though, I was no longer able to resist Angel's badgering. I'd moved in with her soon after we met – that had been a year before, at the '97 festival – and ever since, she'd been on at me to go with her to one of those miracle workshops at which they excel in Glastonbury. Before the accident, I'd had no problem saying no. But now, with that spectral finger hovering between us, it wasn't so easy.

Oh, she knew where I stood on miracles. I'd told her often enough. 'I don't go for any of this new age crap. All these bullshit promises about instant transformation.' At which she'd shout back: 'The world's a mess because of cynics like you. You're a kill-joy. A bloody pessimist.' And I'd think yes, I am. Freud was too. Change comes slow and hard.

But more than ever after that fateful night late in June – though it turned out the finger was lost only to the knuckle – Angel made me feel I owed her something. So, trying not to squirm at what by now seemed the poignant irony of the workshop's invitations – 'Rediscover those lost parts of yourself'; 'Be the whole self you've always dreamt of being' – I rode roughshod over my scepticism and paid for the pair of us. Angel's on a student loan, after all, and lets me stay at her place rent free.

Anyway that was how, on July 12, my dream of creeping off to a mate's house and slumping on the sofa with a stack of spliffs and a six-pack was hijacked by a more girly reality. No World Cup final for me, only a deadly Sunday like those of my childhood. Hours devoted to so-called miracles, then traipsing after Angel down Glastonbury High Street – she a few feet ahead and me like some Moslem wife trailing sulkily behind.

Most people's knowledge of Glastonbury is limited to the pop festival – arms flailing, bodies swaying to Oasis and The Verve in the kind of capacity crowd Wimbledon managers dream of. Festival goers end up too stoned or stony broke to detour into the town, which is a shame because one of the best views of the site is from the whale-backed Tor. A vast patchwork of multi-coloured tents and glittering car roofs stretches over the Somerset levels like a mirrored quilt.

Not that there's much else to recommend the town. It does have its own football team – amateur – who play on the old greyhound track near Godney Road, but that apart, there's fuck all concession to male culture. Glastonbury's devoted to 'higher' things, things of the spirit, and anything to do with men's bodies – sweat, sport, testosterone – gets short shrift.

If that makes me sound more yobbish than I am, blame Angel. Blame the year she spent 'working' on me, accusing me of having a 'closed mind', trying to 'open me up'. Women are so bad at opening things. I suppose it's because they have no technical training. They use tools that are too big for the job, like hacking at a can of beans with a chain-saw. There's no subtlety, no tactics. And whenever Angel came at me with her over-sized blades, I'd just clam shut.

For twelve months we turned round and round in these vicious circles. Angel telling me I was an emotional coward – 'You're like all men. You won't go inward. You won't explore anything you don't know.' Me saying she was too protected from the world – 'Get real, Angel. Get a life.' She would attack me head-on, I would close my defence and she'd be infuriated all the more – 'You're scared, aren't you? Scared of losing yourself. That's why our sex life's no good. You're terrified of being intimate. You're wrapped up. Insulated. You've got a sheath round your heart. An emotional condom.'

And so, time after time, the same goalless draw.

I'm sure living so close to Glastonbury has its effect. The place is so precious, it would bring out the lout in any man. That's why there's such vandalism, lads going on the rampage at night. There has to be some shadow to all that sweetness and light.

To start with, there's no ordinary shops. Nothing as crass as butchers or bakers, only a glut of candlestick-makers to judge by the mountains of wax in every shop window. Store after store stacked with candles, oils, amulets, ankhs, crystals, didgeridoos.

I was restless before I found Angel. I did my share of geo-graphicals. But I can't think of anywhere on earth to compete with Glastonbury for its astral fall-out. Where else could boast such commercial star-dust, such cosmic trivia?

Angel, I'm sorry to say, has been completely seduced. She's besotted with the mythology: King Arthur sleeping in the Abbey grounds; the magic blossoming of the tree on Wearyall Hill where Joseph of Arimathea's supposed to have struck his staff; the miraculous healing waters of the Chalice Well.

It's as though the famous mists of Avalon have risen from the levels like a watery miasma and addled people's brains. There's a legend wrapped like a dog-leg round every lamp-post. The best of men succumb. Even my sometime hero, Billy Blake, couldn't resist. All that fervid stuff in *Jerusalem* – those feet in ancient times walking on England's mountains green – was inspired by Glastonbury. Some myth that Christ himself strode up the Tor.

In fact, though I wouldn't admit this to Angel, ever since I heard that story about Christ coming over here to learn a thing or two from the Druids, I've had a few hallucinations myself. Not that they felt at all visionary. They were utterly convincing, quite as vivid as watching Ginola turn out for Spurs. And yet – incredible though it sounds – a thousand times more beautiful.

I recognised him at once. Who else could it have been – long hair flowing, loose pyjama gown a Persil white? The first couple of times, it was evening. The late sun glanced off his dark skin as he dribbled a ball down Paradise Lane – so graceful, his feet barely skimming the ground. The third time, just after dawn, I hid behind a may hedge. I was worried it might cramp his style, having witnesses – God can't afford to be seen showing off. And within minutes I was rewarded. I stood, gob-smacked, my mouth hanging open. It was all so silent, so effortless. One light move, and he'd spooned the ball high over the Tor in an incandescent arc.

Glastonbury does this to people, gives you weird fantasies, apocalyptic thoughts. That's why it attracts so many spiritual crazies – not just Jesus freaks, but all kinds of cults and sects – Buddhist, Sufi, Hindu, Taoist, Orthodox Jew. Angel, though, has nothing to do with them. She says they're too male-dominated, too 'patriarchal'.

We've had a lot of rows about that word. Me, I can't stand these lazy bits of feminist short-hand, meant to hunch men over, dump the world's gender history on our backs. Like when Angel screams 'You're too male', or 'You're a typical man'.

It would be easier if I wasn't such a sucker for strong women. It's not as if the sex is any better – quite the opposite. No chance of the slam bam thank you mam our fathers got away with, only this protracted trial by orgasm. I suppose it's the plague of the new man.

Not that Angel's a castrating female. No one could be less butch. She's half German – her real name's Angelika (with a hard 'g', not like the green stuff they put in cakes) – and every man who meets her knows why I can't unstick myself. Her Aryan blonde hair curtains her breasts and brushes her waist like a golden veil. She has antelope legs, ethereal skin, turquoise eyes that shimmer like the Holy Grail. Not one unwanted ounce of flesh. And buttocks to die for.

That slow afternoon of the World Cup final, though, I'd had enough self-sacrifice. The miracles workshop had met my worst expectations. As soon as its leader introduced herself – as Shanti – I'd known what kind of day it would be and allowed myself a secret sneer.

It's another Glastonbury hallmark, that no one has an ordinary name. No Pats, Sues or Jills, no Toms, Dicks or Harrys. Only Rams and Sitas, Sanjis and Shaktis, Krishnas and Dirvanas, as if all these exiles from Huddersfield and Surrey have been sea-changed into something – well, if not rich certainly very strange. Their children get branded with the same exotica. The first time I heard a barefoot woman at the belisha beacon yelling 'Ocean! Harmony! Peace!', I thought she was a new wave mental patient released back into community care. Then I saw three toddlers skidding to a halt by the zebra crossing and twigged she'd been calling to her kids.

Anyway, the divine Shanti led us through so many meditations and visualisations, let alone remembrance of things past, I ended up spacey, floating. I felt like a diver after deep immersion, Buzz Aldrin longing for planet earth again.

There was no coffee or booze, only a macrobiotic lunch, and the final straw came when Shanti asked us to share some of our dreams. I declined – it was a bunch of total strangers after all, most of them women – but Angel, her confidence boosted by all these birds of a feather, rushed in and told one of mine for me. It hardly needed interpretation. I'd dreamt my cock was floating several feet in front of me, completely disengaged, then it changed into Angel's lost finger, pointing at me like the 'It could be you!' hand on the Lottery ad.

When the group burst into titters of laughter, that was it. It was quite enough to have missed the game, without adding insult to injury. I'd done my best till then to contain my anger – we all know where male violence can lead – but now I felt like Cantona, provoked beyond my limits, ready to put my boot into the crowd.

So, while the women brewed their final herb teas, I went to the loos and dropped the acid I'd brought with me as a safety valve. It was just starting to take effect as we left the hall and sauntered down the High Street. Angel, who had a nirvana smile on her face, was too blissed out from the workshop to notice my condition. When I lagged behind, she simply paused to wait for me, gazing in the shop windows at the usual Glastonbury mish-mash. It was some minutes before I noticed they were all full of goddesses.

Yes, goddesses. Every shop front was teeming with them, and

the further we walked, the more they seemed to proliferate. Hundreds of naked female figures – a dirty sea green – who squatted in a perfect lotus till they caught sight of me and started to move. Their elegant tapered fingers lifted like sea anemones ready to strike, their siren mouths opened wanting to suck me to death. Their bodies were carved out in the middle, vast bellies hollowed like caves to enclose the unwary. And from the back walls of their wombs, glistening like cats' eyes, shone crystals of amethyst, amber, jade.

'This is what the world needs,' Angel sang at me. 'More of the feminine.'

I would have made a snide remark about the candle-holder cunts – sharp little incisors – but language was already sliding away from me and Angel had moved on.

By now my hearing was heightened too, and I was suddenly struck by the vast silence in the street. It echoed through me as though the end of the world had come. Gone were the familiar shouts of *Big Issue* vendors, gone the music of busking flute players or hammer dulcimers. Gone too the raucous insults of estranged travellers, whose colourful tirades of 'fucking bastard' and 'bleeding slag' so often send nearby traders scooting to the phones for a posse of police, sirens blaring.

No, today, everything was eerily quiet, curfew-still, as if there'd been an order to evacuate the town centre. Even the new age caravan that normally clustered by the railings of St John's church – that crowd of heavily hennaed women and patchouli-oiled men with their mongrels and snotty kids – was gone. I felt a spasm of envy surge through me as I imagined them cosy in their benders, smoking joints and (implausible, I know) watching the match on portable TVs.

But Angel, undisturbed by the peace, was striding on regardless. I followed her reluctantly, re-inventing my walk by clever footwork on the road. Pebbles would multiply to the power of eight, but still I dribbled them round car tyres and hooked them into the nearest drain.

When I realised we'd finally passed the market cross at the bottom of the High Street and entered St Benedict's, I clicked my heels in relief. Like London divided by the Thames, most places have their metaphorical north and south, and here, where incense shops give way to red-bricked terraces, I always feel ordinary life begins again.

Today was a case in point. For though there was still no sight of anyone, the silence was already broken by sounds loudly flying from raised sash windows, open to the balmy summer air. How welcome those sounds were, how familiar in their noisy passion. And how well-orchestrated too, perfectly synchronised from one house to the next. First, that greedy anticipation of pleasure. Then – held for an impossible length of time – a loud intake of breath to signify rapidly mounting bliss. And finally the noisy exhalation of – more often than not – disappointment, incomplete release.

Knowing Angel would only turn it into a reproach, as much as to say *What woman doesn't recognise* that *sound*, I avoided looking at her and concentrated instead on the magenta in a mackerel sky. But as we went further down the road, the noises grew in volume and intensity till with my exaggerated sensitivity, my head was bursting. It sounded as though the whole town was indeed determinedly at it, as though the millennial prophets were right after all and some impending holocaust had driven people to their beds, frantic to net that elusive orgasm before it was lost for all eternity.

Then, just before we reached the car, Angel veered across to the pub, and my heart sank. From the pub's open windows and door the sounds of desire were more strident than ever, and I dreaded the inevitable outburst. I'd learnt with Kate, my previous girlfriend (also a feminist – I know, it's called masochism, it's called substance abuse), there was no point arguing about football. Every time I tried to watch Match of the Day, I'd get a mouthful about it.

'You know what football really is, don't you? It's a displaced sexual activity. Men who can't, watching men who can, bash balls into holes. It's pathetic. A kind of collective rape.'

So I'd decided never to bring it up with Angel. In this at least, football is like faith – you either get it or you don't.

I stood by the kerb, flipping a slim dog turd off the pavement and bracing myself. Angel, of course, with her half German blood, would be more likely to take the racial line. Football as a substitute for war, an up-dated battle between rival clans. If Angel remembered Euro '96, it wouldn't be for the anguish of that heart-stopping penalty shoot-out, but for the xenophobia of the media and fans. I could still hear Kate after the last World Cup, teasing out its tragedy like someone combing a good head for its few grey hairs.

'I don't believe it. Murdering a man for scoring an own goal. How do you think Escobar's family feels now? Christ. When will men grow up?'

I considered my boot, curiously covered with shit. Were all woman like this, I wondered, determined to cap male pleasure? Or was it only beautiful blondes, whose thighs opened like the Red Sea to leave you tiny and drowning?

Then Angel was calling from the pub doorway. 'Hey, we're missing the World Cup final. Didn't you know?'

By the time I'd scraped my foot clean and waded across the pavement in what felt like seven league boots, Angel was already deep in the shadows and smoke. But the shock that followed wasn't simply learning Angel's surprise love of football. No, it was more bizarre than that.

I peered over her shoulders into the gloom. The room was thick with male bodies, only they weren't plural. They were one body, a huge hydra-headed creature whose hundred mouths opened and roared in unison, and whose two hundred eyes glared unblinkingly at a bright flashing screen. The arms – various though they were, stocky and shirt sleeved, tattooed, hirsute, pale – waved like the tentacles of an octopus searching for prey. The back feet stamped like a tethered horse.

And as I watched, to my utter amazement Angel slid into the creature's side as easily as Adam's rib being returned to him. She too jeered and sighed, grabbed a glass of ale that bobbed towards her over a sea of heads like flotsam on the tide and – without taking her wild eyes from the screen – downed it in a series of breathless gulps before absent-mindedly using the back of her hand to wipe the white foam from her upper lip.

I was used to acid, but I'd never hallucinated like this. The screen on which the monster focused was a large black cube, top-heavy on a frail metal perch. And with every fresh blood-thirsty scream, the cube leant more drunkenly towards the floor, vibrating more wildly till I realised it must contain the monster's food and the aim of the gathering was to encourage it to fall.

Inside the box danced the coveted prey, like fish caught in the waters of the screen. They darted constantly to and fro to make capture more difficult. Tiny, lizard-like figures, bunching together one minute, tumbling and tangling like clothes in a washer, only to disperse the next, bolting towards you like screensaver stars that suddenly vanish behind the edges of the frame.

I was already dizzy, somewhere to the side of myself, and this relentless motion made me feel sick. The movements were so fitful, jerky, unpredictable. Not at all the smooth choreographed pattern of a ballet – though some of the postures were clearly failed pirouettes and clumsy pas de deux. No, these were staccato darts that stopped and started, chorused by cheers and jeers, punctured by whistles and shouts.

The sounds came from inside the screen as well as out, as if on the other side of the water lay another whale's belly, equally desperate for prey. These enemy growls also rose and fell in a competing ocean wave. Klaxons hooted, trumpets rasped, tenors sang. Yet not for a second did the lizards stop their display. They span like tops, felled each other like skittles, lay splayed on the ground, their legs opened like scissor blades.

It was Darwinism in reverse, the Origin of Species running backwards. Not beasts struggling to be men, but men nostalgic for their animal ancestry. Why else would these homunculus figures be darting their red tongues, flapping their limbs like grounded birds, dangling from flimsy struts of wood like baby chimpanzees?

Angel was as oblivious to my delirium as she had been to my frustration earlier. She'd barely shot me a grin of delight – 'Brilliant, eh?' – before she'd turned away again, joining the collective groan as a lizard came near to being captured in a net. And when she spoke, I could have been invisible from the way she talked into the air, her eyes never shifting from the squirming figures in the screen.

'You're wondering why I never told you I like football, aren't you? The strange thing is, I'd forgotten myself till today. You know that visualisation we did in the workshop, where we had to think back to a photo of ourselves in the past? I remembered an old newspaper cutting. I'm standing there in my strip, my foot resting on the ball like I'm Columbus conquering the globe. I was in the school team. The only girl.' She back-passed a sexy grin. 'My tackles were second to none.'

She rattled on jauntily, boasting of this triumph, that strike. She knew all the jargon, the virtues of the four-four-two formation versus the three-five-two. But I simply stared at her, dumbfounded, and the more she talked, the more I was hypnotised into silence. It was as though we'd changed places completely – Angel taking to herself what should have been my response, leaving me to inhabit hers. Yes, that was it, I'd turned into a woman surrounded by hysterical men. That was why I felt absent, lost, like water was pressing down on me.

'For a whole season we won every trophy,' Angel gloated. 'We were the top of the county school league.'

But still I could say nothing. Couldn't she see this football was as crazy in its way as all that goddess stuff? That they cancelled each other out?

'It all went wrong when I started dieting,' Angel went on. 'I didn't want to get too big, you see. Too muscular. And I was missing out on men. It wasn't much fun doing circuit training while all my girlfriends were out on dates.' She pulled a wry face. 'So they kicked me out. What else could they do? I'd lost my strength. My crosses were falling short.'

At that moment, another boisterous lurch in the crowd pushed Angel back against me, and those exquisite buttocks were squashed tight into my groin.

'One way or another you see,' Angel murmured, leaning her mouth close to my ear, 'women lose their power.' She flourished the damaged hand with a dash of irony. 'So I shall have to borrow some of yours.'

And taking advantage of the crush, she reached her hand back surreptitiously towards me. I cursed the acid then for its knack of slowing time down. I thought she'd never arrive.

It took years, but there she was, her forgiving hand gently but firmly massaging my cock. And as she pulled me towards her, I knew the workshop had fulfilled its promises. Rediscover those lost parts of yourself? Oh yes. I had the biggest hard-on since Angel and I met.

We didn't wait for the game to finish. We drove up to Glastonbury Tor – happily deserted – and under cover of the ruined tower we fucked away my guilt and Angel's emptiness till we didn't know which one of us was male or female, or who the hell we were.

It was Angel who brought us down to earth. I was still on my back, watching the night sky spin round the Tor, when she stood over me, radiant with pleasure. She rested her foot on my groin

– tenderly, triumphantly – the way she must have looked in that photo all those years before.

'See?' Angel smiled down. 'Miracles do happen.'

Then, seeing I was still glancing upwards, she raised her head. A bleached moon was soaring over a ragged defence of clouds like some great white football lobbed there by my phantom Christ.

'Come on,' Angel said, straightening her clothes. 'We'll find someone who videoed the match.'

Love Among the Turnips

Pete May

Graham Taylor mended my heart. The date was October 13, 1993.
Dave Cantona was on the phone.

'Where are you watching the game then?'

'Well erm, look Dave, I've just realised that I'm supposed to
be going for a drink with this woman from the *New Statesman*. I
thought we might catch it in a pub.'

'What, are you sniffing around lefty women again?' jibed
Cantona.

'No, she's got a sense of humour, honest. Anyway, she's just
someone from work. I've having a sabbatical from lefty women
at the moment.'

'Does she like football?'

'She does since she read Nick Hornby.'

'Well, if she calls herself a footie fan you can get her over to
my mate's house in Clapham.'

'All right then, it is England, I suppose. But remember what
happened in the 1990 World Cup semi-final, Dave. You're a
bad omen. And you're half German. And probably half-Dutch
anyway.'

'My dad's Hungarian. And we're going to lose anyway.'

'I can see it now: Tulips 2 Turnips 0!'

I phoned Bairdy. After all, we were only meeting for a drink,
as friends. She seemed happy enough to come over to Dave's
mate's house. I was sub-editing at the *Statesman* and she was
fund-raising for the John Major libel campaign. We discussed
football. She'd seen a couple of Arsenal games and I'd promised
to try to get her a ticket for West Ham versus Arsenal. She
was just being friendly, I was sure. She wasn't going to be

interested in the Carlton Palmer of the *New Statesman* subs' bench.

I'd enjoyed a reasonably packed fixture programme in the last few years, but always struggled in the play-offs. In the World Cup qualifier of life, Octavia was a 0-1 away defeat to San Marino. She reminded me of John Lyall, always insisting that 'something was missing' before she eventually found the right player at the right price. And he wasn't me. There was one small triumph. In a supremely romantic gesture I presented her with a seventies West Ham shirt. She wore it as a night-dress. Not because it was an incredible turn-on to any Hammers fan; but simply because it was warm.

Siobhan was reminiscent of George Graham. She felt too in control; a disciplinarian wanting to be challenged by a maverick rather than a solid utility player. Seeing Sally was a bit like Howard Kendall's first return to Everton. We performed reasonably well at a mid-table level, but really it proved that, like Howard, you should never go back. And Ruth was stranger than fiction.

It had been two months since Siobhan/George Graham had felt too in control. Women had now been placed below one of those dotted lines that start to appear above the relegation zone on the league tables after Easter. If I hadn't made a title challenge by now it was too late. Who wants someone complaining about you watching a video of *Match of the Day* on Sunday morning, saying that you should be making love, when what you really need is inspiration before playing five-a-side and watching the Sky game?

I met Bairdy after work and we caught the tube to Leicester Square. We were standing in a crowded compartment. I looked down at Bairdy's Kickers and then up to some strange kind of ethnic waistcoat she was wearing. I moved my mouth into action while still wondering why Taylor had played Lee Sharpe at left-back against Norway.

'So what was Nick Hornby like then?'

'He was nice on the phone. He'd just had a baby so he couldn't play football. But he was very supportive to the *Statesman*.'

Bastard, I thought. If only I'd had the idea of writing *Fever Pitch* first.

'Is Wrighty going to play? You can see at Arsenal that he's so much quicker thinking than all the other players,' she continued.

'I think Taylor should select him. As long as Carlton Palmer doesn't play I'll be happy.'

We changed trains at Leicester Square.

'Isn't this the wrong platform?' asked Bairdy.

'Ah, yes. Well done. I was waiting for you to spot that. We should be on the southbound. I must have thought I was going to work . . .' We arrived at Clapham South, bought several cans of beer, and made our way to one of the many uniform houses in seemingly identical streets.

Inside eight people were gathered before a large monitor. Beer cans were being noisily opened. Holland versus England. Rotterdam was a wall of orange. We had to get a result to stand any chance of getting to the US. If we lost we had to beat San Marino 71-0 and Poland do us a favour, or something like that.

'Whoa, footy babe! Is this the missus?' exclaimed Dave Cantona.

'I'm sorry, he's a photographer,' I explained. Bairdy smiled. 'This is Dave Cantona . . .'

By now, Brian Moore was going through the line-ups.

'So is Wrighty playing?' asked Bairdy again.

'No he isn't, which is a strange decision. He's put Merse up front when he's been playing wide all season.'

'Any predictions, Pete? Taylor's Turnips turned over?' said Dave Cantona.

'I think we might get a 0-0,' I said in a fit of pre-match optimism.

The match started surprisingly well. Merson hit a shot just past the post. Dorigo hit the post with a free kick. Holland had a goal disallowed. But maybe we could do it. I was sipping my can of lager.

'Another beer, mate?' asked Dave Cantona at half-time, holding out an inviting can.

'Cheers Dave. Do you remember your huge can in 1990?' I turned to Bairdy. 'He had a massive can of poncey Japanese lager. A big man has a big can. We lost on penalties and it was all his fault.'

'Then everyone went out and trashed BMWs for being German.'

'What can we trash tonight?'

'Florists everywhere. And the National Gallery for exhibiting Van Gogh pictures.'

The second half began. Platt was through when Koeman bought him down on the edge of the area. A collective howl went up in the room.

'Referee! Send him off! That's got to be a penalty!' yelled Dave Cantona. Amazingly the referee let Koeman stay on and England thumped the free-kick into the wall, West Ham-style.

'Dodgy ref or what? He's been bribed,' moaned Dave.

Inevitably Holland went on to score. An almost identical free-kick outside the English area. They too slam it into the wall. But the man in black orders it to be retaken.

'They'll score now,' I groaned to Bairdy. 'It's just like watching West Ham.'

'Again it's Ronald Koeman. Again the problem is there. Again it's a critical moment. He's going to flick one,' said Brian Moore. 'He's going to flick one . . .'

'I think he's going to flick one,' said Dave Cantona.

'He's going to flick one – and it's in!' finished Brian.

'Fuck . . .' I sighed

'Fucking Koeman! He should have been off!' someone cursed.

Merson hit the post to emphasise that a malevolent deity was against England. Then Bergkamp danced through the England defence and planted a shot inside Seaman's near post. During the final ten minutes Taylor began making strange winding actions with his hands, pacing the touchline and harassing the linesman as a bemused FIFA official tried to persuade him to return to the dugout.

'That man's lost it,' said Bairdy.

I was impressed. Clearly she knew a deranged England boss when she saw one.

'Look at Taylor. What is he on?' shouted Dave Cantona.

'And I don't think I've ever seen Graham Taylor so upset,' commented Brian Moore in his phlegmatic the-England-boss-might-be-raging-like-King-Lear-but-I'll-pretend-everything's-normal voice.

Someone threw an empty beer can at the TV. The final whistle blew. The vegetables had been roasted.

We gathered our coats. Bairdy and myself left for the tube station. It was a dreary ride back north. It's strange how after an emotionally draining game you feel physically tired. Jean-Paul Sartre could write a whole book on football nausea.

'Of course, we lost it by drawing at Wembley, really,' I mumbled.

I couldn't think of romance.

'I wish it could have been a better game. Still, there's always 1998. I'll see you at work, we'll have to have a proper drink before you go away,' I said as I made for the tube door. I tried to kiss her on the cheek but missed. Rather like England.

Three weeks later Bairdy phoned. Her approach was very Graham Taylor and decidedly Route One. Was she really suggesting what I thought she was to me, Carlton Palmer?

I saw a vision of a rotund man in a crumpled England tracksuit. As if inspired by the spirit of our great leader, I decided: 'We'll get Bairdy on. We'll give Bairdy a go.' Turnips 1, Swede Nothings 0. The rest is her story. Did I not not like that.

The People's Game

Tom Bromley

January, 1997. Millbank Towers, the home of the Labour media machine. The place where spin doctors made Blair look good, Prescott intelligent, Robin Cook a man capable of an interesting sex life. Banks of computers logged every Tory statement, searched for every possible discrepancy. Activists manned phones, phoned men, women, anyone who might vote Labour. A huge poster said 'Enough is Enough', though that was thought to be a reference to D:Ream, on the tannoy twenty-four hours a day.

Jeremy desperately wanted to believe that things could only get better. He had two dreams in life: Labour to get elected, England to win the World Cup. Both had let him down miserably over the years. From Stuart Pearce's penalty, to Taylor picking Carlton Palmer. From 'Crisis? What Crisis?', to Kinnock shouting 'We're all right!' From Ray Wilkins' sending-off, to Walker's foul on Overmars. From Micheal Foot's donkey jacket, to Harriet Harman's existence. Labour's lead in the polls was high, but he couldn't help but feel tense. It was England vs Germany all over again, with Tony Blair as Gareth Southgate.

Jeremy had entered Millbank straight after university. He'd worked for the Rapid Rebuttal Unit, then for Audience Participation. Two weeks into his post, he suggested fixing the *Today* poll for Blair and was picked for greater things. Officially working for the Key Seats Campaign, in reality he joined the Does Not Exist Unit. A crack group of four, the DNE did dirty tricks, things not acceptable, thought the unthinkable. Their brief was to get Labour votes by all means necessary, bribery and violence excepted.

'Sorry I'm late.' Jeremy shut the door behind him, drowning out the sound of D:Ream. The room was small, poky, not much bigger than the broom cupboard everyone else thought it was. He sat down next to Martin, a freelance tabloid hack. Martin's top button was permanently undone, his tie skewed to the right. Opposite was Stephen, an ex-scriptwriter for Jim Davidson, whose floppy fringe was marginally shorter that Jeremy's. To his left was Anthony, a New Labour, old Labour, whichever way was in Labour sort of a guy. As always, he wore one of Blair's castoff ties, won at a charity auction.

'Coffee?' Anthony asked. 'It's Nescafé, I'm afraid, we've run out of . . .' He passed Jeremy a mug.

New Labour, new lad. The DNE was brainstorming ways of getting such people to the polling box, without resorting to putting a line of coke on the side. They weren't anti Labour, according to research, just anti giving a fuck. As long as the government didn't ban *Baywatch*, they weren't too bothered who was in power. If the DNE could haul in the votes, they might just swing enough marginals to make up a majority.

'So what have you got for me?' Anthony asked. 'Who wants to start? Martin?'

'Skirts,' said Martin, 'or lack of them to be precise. Whenever Labour gets into power, the skirts get shorter, mini skirts come back in fashion. Happened in the sixties, the seventies, too. Now obviously we'd have to handle this carefully. Short, Harman, that lot, they're not going to like it, so a few well placed articles, pseudonyms of course. Plus photos, lots of them, there's a couple of activists downstairs I think would be perfect. Vote Labour, vote Leg, that kind of thing. New Labour, Nude Britain.'

'Not bad. These articles, they'd go in, what?'

'*Loaded, Playboy, Readers' Wives, Neighbours' Wives, The Wife of the Bloke at Number 37 . . .*'

'I think you'll find it's 39,' Anthony said, embarrassed.

'No, that's a different magazine. *Number 37* is straight porn, whilst *Number 39* involves the use of small . . .'

'Maybe we'll move on at this point.' Anthony's face was a distinctly old Labour red. 'Stephen?'

'Music, Anthony, that's the answer.' Stephen coughed. 'All the best music happens under a Labour government. Let's start with sixty-four to seventy. The best Beatles albums, the Kinks, the Stones, the Who, the golden era of British music. Then you get the early seventies, Tory government, Glam Rock, Prog Rock, even Slade. Labour get back in power, you get the Pistols, the Clash, punk rock, new wave. The eighties, synth land, new romantics, Simply Red . . .'

'Stephen, the boss likes Simply Red . . .'

'You're kidding me? Well, OK, Simple Minds then. Up to date and we're looking at a global breakthrough for British music. Radiohead, The Prodigy, Oasis, they're all going to have massive albums this year. Symbolic of a new, young dynamic Britain. Think of the radio ad campaign you could have with that lot. New Labour, New Wave of New Wave of New Wave.'

'Hmm.' Anthony took a sip of coffee, thought for a second. 'Jeremy, Martin? What do you think?'

'It could work,' said Martin, 'but you'd have to be careful. I mean "Anarchy in the UK", it's not exactly tough on crime, is it?'

'I don't think the boss would buy it,' said Jeremy. 'Have you seen his choice for *Desert Island Discs*? It's all Free and Bruce Springsteen. He actually *likes* music from the early seventies.'

Anthony was nodding, making notes whilst Jeremy talked. 'I think that's right, I'm afraid, Stephen. If the boss had better taste in music, things might be different. Jeremy, it's your turn.'

Jeremy looked at his notes and smiled, the smile of a man who only had David James to beat.

'OK Anthony, this one you'll like. It's building on all that crap Blair spouted at the conference, Labour's coming home and all that. The thesis is, and I've checked this out, that when Labour do well, the England football team do well. Very well in fact, World Cup-winning form as it goes. Remember that famous shot, of Harold Wilson on the hotel balcony with the 1966 team? All we need to do is to convince people that the two are linked.

'The next government, Ted Heath, a disaster for English football. Labour should have won the election in 1970, to everyone's surprise they lose. In the World Cup, a couple of months later, England are two up against West Germany, substitute Charlton and Peters. Like Labour, they throw it away. The next World Cup we qualify for, 1982, and Britain is ruled by the Tories again. We don't lose, but fail to score in our last two games. The overriding image, a negative one, is Keegan fluffing his header against Spain. A missed opportunity, something at Labour we know all about.

'1986, the main memory is a negative image again. Not Lineker's hat-trick against Poland, or Maradona's mesmerising goal. It's the Hand of God, or the Hand of Cheating Little Shit as I like to call it. A symbol, you'll like this, of the injustice of the Thatcher years. We knew we'd been wronged but could do nothing about it. 1990 . . .'

'1990.' Anthony grinned. 'Now I remember this one. England were great.'

'No, England were terrible. We shouldn't need extra time to beat Belgium. Or two penalties to get past Cameroon. We played well against Germany, but their goal, well, a terrible sod's law deflection, the sort we seem to be permanently stuck with. What people remember, though, and this is what counts, is Gazza crying, and Waddle shooting into the stratosphere. Like the rest of the images from the Thatcher years, they're ones of despair.'

'And then we got John Major.'

'And football got Graham Taylor. An eye for an eye, a jerk for a jerk. Did we not like that? We failed to qualify for the States, fuck, we even get *beaten* by them.' Jeremy winced as the thought of 'Yanks 2, Planks 0' ran through his head. 'Then we get to Terry Venables, the John Smith figure in all this, laying the foundations for Hoddle like Smith did for Blair. Labour look electable, England do well in Euro '96, but can't win because Major is still in charge. They lose to Germany wearing Major's favourite colour.

'So now, 1998 is looming. The grey kit has been swapped for a red one. If Labour get in, it'll be the first time we've contested a final under them since 1966. Now this may seem spurious to you, but any real football fan, desperate for England to win, if there's anything they can do, however small it seems, believe me, they'll do it.'

'Jeremy, are you suggesting that people will vote Labour because they are superstitious enough to believe it might help England win the World Cup?'

'Why else would they vote Labour?'

'Jeremy, what about Scotland?' Martin had been brought up in Glasgow. 'Where do they fit into all this?'

Jeremy shrugged.

'Scotland are the Liberal Democrats of international football. Always there, but never actually win anything. Besides, it's England where we need the votes.' He thought for a moment. 'We could do a Scottish campaign if you like, I don't know, promise they'll get past the first round or something.'

'Be serious,' said Stephen. 'I thought we were meant to offer promises we could keep.'

'Look,' said Jeremy, 'if you're looking for a wider campaign there's stuff that fits with New Labour philosophy. There's all these great parallels about England doing well when we have a proper team. When England work round a single individual, Gazza, or Johnny Haynes in 1962, then we're up shit creek. When we're a *team* we stand a chance. You could use that to tap into all that bollocks about community.'

'The boss might like this.' Anthony nodded. 'We'll meet again on Thursday. I want more info, videos, a slogan . . .'

'I've got one of those already,' said Jeremy.

'What's that?'

'The People's Game.'

Thursday. Jeremy was in a good mood after picking Michael Portillo on the sweepstake for next Tory leader. He'd made a great video montage of classic England failures under Tory governments. The 6-3 defeat by Hungary (1953), the one-all draw with Poland (1973), the 2-1 defeat by Norway (1981), the 2-0 win for the US (1993). In the corner of the screen was the Graham Taylor turnip, replaced with a John Major one. For sound he'd chosen a particularly turgid slice of progressive rock, and that commentary from the Norway game: 'Maggie Thatcher, can you hear me? Maggie Thatcher, your boys took a hell of a beating!' Then the music cut to a sixties riff, shots of Geoff Hurst, Bobby Moore, Nobby Stiles, Harold Wilson, mini skirts, the Beatles getting their MBEs . . . Then the caption

> *England have only ever won the World Cup under a Labour government.*
> *Football: the People's Game. Labour: the People's Party.*

'What's up?'

Anthony appeared, looking angry.

'I got William fucking Hague in the sweepstake, didn't I? I thought we'd agreed, no joke candidates.'

Jeremy played him the video. He showed him a press pack, about the great teams of the 1940s. Attlee , Bevan, Bevin . . . Lawton, Wright, Matthews. As Labour revolutionised the country, England scored 72 times in 19 matches. Won 10-0 in Portugal. 4-0 in Italy. He showed Anthony proposals to make England more New Labour. The shirts to be redesigned by Alexander McQueen. The three lions to be replaced by sharks in formaldehyde. Blur and Oasis to co-write the official song (Mo Mowlam might be needed here). Jeremy had written a joke too, about how the football team would be bereft of ideas, but give great press conference. He left this out.

'I'm sorry, Jeremy.' Anthony looked apologetic. 'M says it's no go. The mini skirts he likes, reckon it could get us the endorsement of the *Sunday Sport*. The football is out. M says politics and sport don't mix. Look at Hitler and the 1936 Olympics. Argentina and the 1978 World Cup. It's a tactic only used by right-wing, authoritarian leaders . . .'

Jeremy pulled a face.

'Also we've got to stick to promises we can deliver. Not raising taxes is one thing, winning the World Cup is another. We did think about it, really, even the boss was consulted. I think their problem isn't the concept, it's the choice of sport. Football apparently is not New Labour. There's other sports we should focus on, that are more in tune with New Labour thinking.'

'Other sports?' Jeremy asked. 'Like what?'

'Jeremy, have you heard of a guy called Bernie Ecclestone . . .'

Where I Go When You're Watching the World Cup

Maureen Freely

Church Row. I go back to Church Row. Every single time, no matter who's playing, that's where I go. If you want to know the whole story, I'll need to take you back to 1966, to a cold, clear Sunday afternoon in November. It's a quarter to one, the bells in the Church Row church have just gone, and I'm passing alongside the cemetery where Daphne du Maurier's father is buried. A few paces ahead of me is a woman with a mane of straight brown hair that swings as she walks and a mauve mini coat with matching boots that click. She glances at her watch as she reaches my beloved Georgian terrace. As she draws level with the third house, the house I want to live in when I grow up, she pauses to peer into the dark front room, then looks at her watch and moves on.

She pretends to take an interest in the other darkened front rooms as she passes them, and as I slow my own steps to avoid passing her, I do the opposite. I try to look in without looking interested. I train the corner of my eye on the frosted windowpanes and try to see beyond them without moving my head. But I do something wrong, because now the woman in the mauve minicoat glances over her shoulder to look at me and then crosses to the other side of Church Row.

As she doubles back in the direction of the church and the cemetery, she looks at me, straight in the eyes this time, and her lip curls. Has she noticed that I'm wearing a navy gabardine school coat? If so, has she asked herself why any one would be caught dead in a navy gabardine school coat on a weekend? My classmates wouldn't be caught dead wearing a navy gabardine school coat – not even if it's a weekday and they're on their way to school. My mother insists it looks like a fashionable weekend coat now that she's hemmed it. But she forgot to do whatever you're supposed to do to a vent to make it hang straight. So now it sticks out like a ducktail at the back and when I look at my reflection in the plate glass windows of the Express Dairy, it's the first thing I see.

It follows me all the way up Heath Street and down Hampstead High Street. As I make my way back along Perrin's Walk, it seems to me that the two men sitting behind my reflection in the offices of the *Ham & High* are laughing because my ducktail looks so funny, and so I find a bench, and try to flatten out the ducktail by sitting on it, but as I head down Church Row again, I glance at my reflection in the window of the wooden house just beyond the Express Dairy and see it's sticking out even more than before. I pause to steel myself for the ordeal ahead. How to get to the other end of the terrace without anyone else seeing it? I opt for walking at an angle, so that the ducktail is not part of my imagined silhouette. But my precautions are unnecessary. As I come up to the first Georgian house I look into the front room to see it has become a brilliant world unto itself.

A man with a handlebar mustache and a scarlet waistcoat is opening a bottle of champagne while a large supporting cast looks on. They are all shapes, all ages and sizes, all dressed in brocades and silks and velvets. There is not a single one who isn't beautiful, not a single one who doesn't look at home. And it's the same in the next house, where a dark-eyed pouting woman with one of those slanted Mary Quant haircuts has come to the window to drape her arms around a man who is wearing a polka dot tie. He has a head of golden curls, and so do two of the three men who are standing next to the fireplace in the third sitting room, raising their glasses for a toast. In the houses on the other side of the road, it's the same scene ten times over. In window after window after window, party after party after party. It's the Natural History Museum of Sunday Lunch.

And now, as I approach the third house from the end of the

terrace, the house I plan to make my own one day, I can see the woman in the purple minicoat ringing the bell. A man opens the door, and a rush of laughter escapes through it. 'Juliet!' the man cries. 'At last! We were beginning to lose hope!' 'Oh, I am sorry,' she says. 'It's that Northern Line. You have to allow so much time for it on a Sunday.' 'Oh, I know, I know,' says the man. 'But you're here now, that's all that matters.' And he ushers her in, and the door closes. I stop outside the window to watch a sea of flushed faces look up to welcome Juliet. Whom they haven't seen since . . . when? Where? To whom they are now telling such a funny little story about . . . what?

This is my first year in England. We're here because my father's on sabbatical. There is no plan for a second year. I've just turned fourteen, and it's partly because I look twelve that my abiding memories of this year are of standing outside. Standing outside cinemas that won't admit me . . . yet. Standing outside nightclubs where my older-looking classmates are practically lodgers, asking myself how much longer? How many centuries of agony before I am over-age in the eyes of that bouncer? Standing with my sister and brother outside the Flask, the Bird in Hand, and Jack Straw's Castle, waiting for our mother to bring us out crisps that will make our fingers even colder.

But not as cold as they become when I'm standing in the middle of a playing field in Hendon, breathing frost on a hockey stick as I struggle to figure out what the rules are. Or when I'm hovering outside Kenwood House in roller-skates, knowing what the rules are about roller skates indoors but feeling so cold they don't matter any more. Or when my mother and father and sister and brother and I are walking back and forth, back and forth, outside a restaurant called The Keats. We're not just cold this time, we're hungry. After five evenings at the opera and a lost weekend in Dublin, my parents have run through the grant money too fast again this month, and now we can't even afford to buy butter. But there's a little blue warrior in the left-hand corner of the window in the door, so my father says the hell with it, and we all troop into The Keats and order double courtesy of American Express. On the way home we do a Greek line dance all the way up Hampstead High Street. We pass an Indian restaurant, and when a man eating alone at a table next to the window catches sight of us, he drops his spoon.

Next to the Indian restaurant is a shoe shop where there isn't a single shoe that isn't yellow or pink. It's the same in all the shoe shops that spring. It's yellow, pink, or nothing. And if you don't have a cape, you can forget it. The best ones are lined and have little slits for your arms. I remember standing in a bus queue where even the dog is wearing a cape I could kill for. After a long campaign, I get my own. It doesn't have a lining, or little slits for my arms, but it releases me from the curse of the ducktail. I go out for a walk of triumph. And then, when I'm standing at the crosswalk on Heath Street with my trophy swirling around me, a French boy comes up to me and tells me I'm despicable because I belong to the bourgeoisie.

Does he intend it as an insult? It's not the way I take it. My heart is still pounding as I climb the wrought iron staircase that leads to our flat on the corner of Church Row and Frognal Gardens. The kitchen window is open. I can hear my mother doing the dishes as she listens to *The Archers*, and as I ask myself: if I look bourgeois does that mean there is some hope for me? I don't have many memories like this: I seem to have spent most of the year standing outside on our roof garden, sulking. Sometimes it's because my father has turned off the television, because he can't bear the sight of Jimi Hendrix biting his guitar. Other times it's because my mother is in hospital and my father has brought all his pub cronies back, or because one of them, Alan Grouse, forever after known as Alan Louse, has pissed on the sofa, or because my father has burned same sofa while trying to dry it with an electric heater in time for my mother's return. I am out of sorts already, because Radio London is playing *Sergeant Pepper* for the first time and halfway through my transistor radio has died on me. But then before I know it, I'm forgetting my growing pains because I'm so caught up in the garden party that our landlord the choirmaster is giving in the garden below, or because I'm trying to count how many butlers there are in the other party going on in the larger, grander garden on the other side of the fence. I remember forgetting myself in the same way as I stand outside the graveyard, as I try to imagine what Daphne du Maurier's father looked like, but never so much as when I'm standing outside the houses in Church Row on Sunday lunchtime, wondering what you had to do to get inside and what you did once you got there, trying to guess what they all thought was so funny, and desperate to get in on the joke.

Four years later, I get a chance to find out. We're back in London, but only for a week. We're staying at the Post House Hotel in Belsize Park, where one of my old classmates has a job as a bellboy. Without quite understanding what is eating me, he is happy enough to come along to Jack Straw's Castle, and the Flask, and the Holly Bush, and the Bird in Hand, and the Swiss Cottage Odeon, and any other building we happen to pass that I remember once denied me entry. When he's on duty, I've been catching up on films. I get through *Woodstock*, *The Go-Between*, and *They Shoot Horses, Don't They?* in the first two afternoons.

And now it's Saturday, a sunny Saturday afternoon in late August. I'm walking into the church on Church Row to attend a wedding. The Canadian brother and sister who've brought me are not, strictly speaking, friends. They're cousins of a friend whose parents' summer house is next door to my parents' summer house in Naxos. When these cousins were visiting Naxos earlier in the summer, I happened to mention to them that I used to live off Church Row, and they said, 'Church Row! How amazing! Our best friends are getting married at the church on Church Row at the end of August!' When it emerged that I would be in London at the same time, they offered to take me along.

But now they may be regretting their generosity, because

already I've teamed up with another friend of theirs who is out of her skull on something. I'm the only one who doesn't mind. Does this mean that my romance with the bourgeoisie is over, and I've finally resigned myself to the bohemian fate my parents always wanted for me? My new friend and I sit right behind the bride's unamused relatives and blow bubbles throughout the service. 'Honestly, Belle, when are you going to grow up?' the bride says to her afterwards. But to me she is perfect politeness.

The reception is not on Church Row but on Frognal, on the large, grand lawn I would look down on with such longing from our roof garden when we lived on the other side of the fence. The butlers have multiplied in our absence and they give me too much champagne. When I wake up the next morning, I have three phone messages from someone called Dave, four messages from two different Roberts, and another from a James in Sussex. I also have a headache. So I go for a walk, and as I turn into Church Row, I see a man and a woman coming out of one of the houses. The man breaks into a smile and waves. Wasn't I speaking to him last night in the dinner queue? Is he the one who caught me when I lost my balance? The woman looks familiar, too, but she does not smile as she tugs his other arm and pulls him back into the house, which turns out to be the third house from the end of the terrace, the house I was going to make my own one day. There is a weaker smile and smaller wave from the man as the dark corridor engulfs him. Then a female arm reaches out of it and the door slams shut.

Push ahead to 1978. I've been through university by now, and worked my way through a string of unsuccessful secretarial jobs. I've written two novels but have yet to see anything in print. I'm two years into a marriage that is not yet on the rocks. I'm also three months pregnant. The flat we are renting is on Belsize Park Gardens, right across the street from the North Vietnamese Embassy and less than five minutes' walk from the Post House

Hotel. It's a warm and sunny June evening and we're just heading up to The Flask to meet up with an Argentinian painter friend, and as I stand on the pavement, waiting for my husband to join me, I want to make the most of the weather, but my eyes won't cooperate. They're glued to the ground-floor flat next door. There's a sofa next to the window, and sitting on it are three small children. They've just had their bath and now their mother is putting on their pyjamas. How many years before I can do the same? When will my life begin? What do I have to do to get to the other side of the window?

I've watched them before, so I know what happens next: half an hour of children's television and then bedtime, no ands, ifs or buts. But today there is a glitch in their routine. Their father comes into the room and changes the channel to the football. Then he has the children move over to make room for him. They protest. Their mother hears them and comes back into the room wearing a tired, brittle smile. 'Darling, do you really . . .?' He waves her away. 'It's not just any match!' he says. 'It's the World Cup!' She makes a sharp remark, her voice louder now, but I can't hear the end of her sentence because now there's a goal, it must be a goal for the wrong side, because the husband jumps up and howls like a wounded animal. I don't get to see the outcome, but as we walk up Belsize Park Gardens, there are more howls and whistles flowing through every open window.

We've been at The Flask for a good half-hour and my husband is into his third or fourth drink by the time Gerardo, our Argentinian painter friend, arrives. He is carrying a small portable television, and he's brought another Argentinian painter friend with him, and all they can talk about is the World Cup. They're not making much sense, because they've been at the French pub all afternoon. But eventually I work out that Argentina is going to be playing Hungary that evening, and that they're determined not to miss it.

The second Argentinian painter, whose name is also Gerardo, tells us it's essential that they have a Chinese meal beforehand,

and so he takes us and the television set along to his studio, which is a few houses away from the Flask and has only three paintings in it. One is of a pint of Guinness, another is a portrait of a man looking at a ghost in a mirror, and the third features a vamp brandishing a marble hammer and sickle. The banner over her head says, 'Te Espero en Siberia, Mi Amor'. It's a 'serious joke', he tells me, and he hands me a wok. The two painters pick up the television, my husband finishes his fifth or sixth drink and takes the aerial, and off we go to Gerardo the Second's house, which turns out to be none other than the third house from the end of the terrace on Church Row.

Gerardo the Second does not notice that I have stopped breathing. He pushes open the door as if it were just a door. He leads us through a white hallway and down a white staircase into a kitchen that doesn't bear a single trace of its former occupants. It is as clean and featureless as a display room in a kitchen factory. 'Maria, we need you!' cries Gerardo the Second in a voice that is both peeved and dictatorial. 'Maria, where are you?' he shouts when she does not jump from the shadows. She takes her time to move her large bulk into the light. Maria, I soon work out, is the maid Gerardo and his wife have brought with them from Ecuador. She stands with beady eyes and arms akimbo as her employer tries to cut up vegetables. When they end up on the floor, she swoops down to retrieve them. When he spills the oyster sauce on the counter, she is there with a damp cloth so fast he also spills it on her hand. She does not approve of the contents of the wok, but at the same time she seems pleased to be watching a man cook badly. She does not let him serve. She has just removed herself to her observation post at the counter next to the window when we are joined by a slim, elegant, woman I take to be Gerardo's wife. She is not at all pleased to meet us.

'Where have you been?' she asks her husband in Spanish as she smoothes her napkin over her lap. 'Where do you think?'

is his answer. I only catch one word – tonto – in her rapid-fire reply. He throws it back at her. She does the same. He stands up as if to make a speech, but then Maria the maid says, 'Sit down and eat your food while it's hot!' Without another word, he obeys her. We finish the meal in silence. Then our host picks up the television set and orders Maria to follow with wine and glasses, the wife, whose name is Marisela, jumps up and barks 'No traiga nada!'

Upstairs in yet another bare room, I try to make myself comfortable in a folding chair Maria has opened for me and when the silence has gone on too long I try to make conversation. 'How did you come to be living on Church Row?' I ask the wife. She lets out a sharp laugh. Her husband joins in. 'That's another serious joke.' The wife laughs again. 'Yes, very serious,' she says. At this point, the phone rings. Maria the maid gives Marisela the wife an enquiring look, but the wife says, 'No, let it ring. He's beginning to get on my nerves. Let him suffer for once.' Maria the maid nods in obedience, and the phone keeps ringing. On the twentieth ring or so, Gerardo the Second turns to his wife and says, 'Mi amor. Would you like me to do the honours?' She considers his request as the phone continues ringing. Then she stands up and says. 'No, I'd better take care of him myself. If he's persisting this long, it must be serious.'

She leaves the room. The phone stops ringing. Happy again, our host puts on a record. It's a collector's item, apparently – a famous Cuban satirical pianist from the thirties or forties. I can hardly understand a word, but the two Gerardos have never heard anything so funny. Then the wife comes back, and she can't keep a straight face either, and she falls back into a bean bag in the corner and calls for Maria to pour her a glass of wine, and then the record ends and the television goes on, and the match is just beginning, and the wife lifts her glass and says, 'Down with Hungary!'

It's clear from the response she gets from the two Gerardos that this is not just a serious joke, but one with several levels. No one takes me to one side to explain, but it doesn't matter. It's enough to be here. I know all I need to know to appreciate my good fortune, and so I can sit back and relax and watch this strange group of friends watch Argentina take on Hungary. It doesn't matter that I don't know what they're up to. What matters is that all over the world, people are watching the same thing we're watching, and not a single one of us knows what will happen next.

So why should I expect to know any better? Why would I even want to? Sooner or later, I'll get the joke, I tell myself – and I'm right. A few weeks later, when I happen to be walking down Church Row, I see from the heavy drapes and the abundant furniture just visible through the dark front windows that the house has changed hands again. It turns out Gerardo the Second and his wife were interlopers just like me. The house never really belonged to them. It was a gift from the wife's very old, very wealthy, Hungarian lover. She did something to slight him not long after our visit, or maybe even during our visit, and that was that. They moved on to the next disaster, and so did I. I've never been back – except in my mind, of course. As I said, it's where I go whenever you're watching the World Cup.

I go there between times, too. I save it for special occasions. It's one of those set pieces I return to if I'm feeling agitated and need to calm myself down in a hurry. What I do is close my eyes and put the scene together figment by figment. First the bare white walls and the branches resting against the windows. Then the bean bags and the folding chairs and the black phonograph on the far wall. Maria the maid enters the room with five wineglasses on a silver tray. Marisela the wife says something insulting about Hungary and the two Gerardos laugh. My husband smiles at me and I smile back because I still love him, because I'm expecting his child, because I do not know he'll getting out of bed in the middle of the night to go to the Victoria Sporting Club.

But that doesn't matter. At least it doesn't matter to me now. What matters is that I don't feel locked out any more. The door has flown open and ushered me in, and now here I am, sitting on the cusp of the future. All I have to do from here on in is trust it. All I have to is close my eyes and wish.

And so that's what I do. I close my eyes and then there's a roar from the portable television on the bookcase. I look up to see that Argentina have just turned the tables on Hungary with only a few seconds left on the clock. That is how I remember it, that is how I'll always remember it, even though my diary says we left the house before the match even began.

The Man of Paper

Nick Rogers

Cleopatra: Come, you'll play with me, sir?
Mardian: As well I can, madam.
Shakespeare

CHAPTER I

BAD GIRL

The dressing room was filled with the odour of liniment and leather, Peppino was sprawled on the treatment table and I – I was sitting astride his lap. Above and beyond the locked dressing room door, daubed with Signor Pozzo's graffito 'NO HANDS' we could hear the shuffle and hubbub of the cap-sleeved crowd, gathering in the warm Florentine sun.

'*Cap-sleeved*? Never mind. Peppino, listen and repeat. *I want you.*'

'You want me.'

'Don't be a sap! The other way. *I want you.*'

'I want you.'

'Correct. And? . . . *And*? Peppino?'

And deftly, with infinite patience, his strong brown hands unwound my fox fur stole . . .

. . . but just when it was starting to get really good, there was a rap at the door and a big voice boomed:

'Peppino, Signorita! Open up.'

It was six long weeks since Vittorio Pozzo, the dapper, silver-haired *Commissario Tecnico* of the *Azzurri*, had taken his team into *ritiro* in the Tuscan watering hole of Roveta. I was installed as 'maître d'hôtel' at the HQ (a barracks-like building, solid and squat, encircled by velvety hills) and each night, after dinner, Pozzo would take me aside and whisper the orders: 'Fifteen minutes each, Olivia. Ten for Orsi. And mind Monti's toe.' Then I'd tie on a pinny and do my rounds. For the first few days I just sat there wittering on, about, whatever, anything, basically, to help establish some sort of social and cultural setting: synthetic detergent, the discovery of induced radioactivity, the blithe surrealism of economic ruin, German rearmament, American movies (*King Kong, She Done Him Wrong, Dinner At Eight*), Aldo Palazzeschi's cunning new novel *Sorelle Materassi*, the unjustly imprisoned brigand Giuseppe Musolino, Luigi Pirandello's return from self-exile, the suicide of the director George 'The Big House' Hill, the birth of the actress Sophia Loren, even (this didn't touch them too deeply) Ramsay MacDonald's failing health. Anyroad, with that out of the way, one thing led to another, and I soon grew fond of Pozzo's tireless team, and very fond of Ambrosian-Inter's young centre-forward, Giuseppe 'Peppino' Meazza: quick, subtle and, although not tall, most effective with his head . . .

Now, following the first round thrashing of the United States, the *Azzurri* were to be put to their first real test of the tournament: the quarter-final against Spain and Ricardo Zamora, their near-legendary 33-year-old goalkeeper and captain.

'Peppino, Signorita! Open up.'

I unlocked the door and ten men filed in. Shall I give you the team? In goal, the captain, Giampiero Combi, 31, funny, bright and acrobatic, since 1930–31 the winner of four consecutive *Serie A* titles with Juventus. At right-back Bologna's Eraldo Monzeglio, 27, sensual, spiritual and tenacious in the tackle, brought in by Pozzo for the cool but complicated Rosetta. At left-back Peppino's Inter team-mate Luigi Allemandi, 28, sincere, okay-looking, once banned for life after being accused of accepting a bribe . . . absurd! The half-back Pizziolo, 27, the engine of the engine-room, if you like, and Roma-Fortitude's Attilio Ferraris IV, 30, as imperious on the pitch as he was intense behind the bar he ran in Rome: a forty-a-day smoker until Pozzo calmly persuaded him to cut down. At centre-half, Juve's ball-winning dispatcher Luisito Monti, 32: an absolute bastard but just about resistible, he played for Argentina in the 1930 World Cup final and lost. One of three *oriundo* in the side besides the two wingers, the cute, genuinely single (great for team-spirit) Guaita, 28, at outside-right, and on the left Juve's Raimondo 'Mumo' Orsi, 32, muscular, fast, slim and, on 10,000 lire a month with an explosive left foot shot, a little too aware of his pulling power. At centre-forward (Pozzo preferred to play Peppino at inside-right) Bologna's big, happy, balanced Angiolino Schiavio, 28. And at inside-left, the rangy, sweet-faced Gioanin Ferrari, 26, the fourth Juventus player in the side, who, after missing a memorable sitter on his debut versus Switzerland in 1930, was proving to be one of Pozzo's most indispensable players.

I rubbed my hands.

'Could you leave us alone for a few minutes?' asked Combi politely.

I slunk out of the room, swept down the tunnel and into the Stadio Berta . . .

CHAPTER II

MEN

Italy started brightly, with Monti not unfortunate to stay on the pitch, but were denied the goal they deserved by a string of fine saves from Zamora. Then in the fortieth minute, against the run of play, the Spanish took the lead. Langara's quickly taken free-kick was turned in by Regueiro, his miss-kick deceiving Combi. With the second-half less than a minute old Italy drew level. Meazza, clean through on Zamora, was cynically tripped from behind. Ferrara controlled Pizziolo's floated free-kick on his chest, flicked it over a ball-watching defender with his right foot, and rammed it past Zamora with his left. Good. The Azzurri piled on the pressure in search of the winner. Zamora made a few more decent saves, I suppose, the match went into extra-time, and the Spanish hung on grimly to force a draw. But the referee had given the Italians so little protection that four of the side (and to be fair, seven Spaniards, including Zamora, who at his advanced age failed to recover from a couple of cracked ribs) were unable to take part in the replay which took place the following day. It didn't matter: the Azzurri swept through to the semi-final thanks to a glorious glancing header from an ebullient Meazza.

CHAPTER III

PALS IN PARADISE

Before the Great War, the young Pozzo came to London to learn English, found 'too many Italians looking for one another and spending evenings with each other', and so moved farther north, to Borchester, or near enough, to be amongst the English. When his family ordered him home, he refused, and they cut off his allowance. But Pozzo was a ripping linguist and made up for it by teaching languages all over the Midlands. On Saturdays he travelled up to Old Trafford to watch Manchester United. *Why*? Because he admired United's rugged centre-half, Charlie Roberts, an all-round, attacking player who would launch the ball far out to the wings. One dull dark afternoon after a dour scoreless draw, Roberts felt a tap on his shoulder. Pozzo introduced himself and asked whether the great man might like to talk to him about football. After some hesitation, Roberts agreed. It was the first of many conversations over a good honest pint in Roberts' local in Hulme. Or perhaps I'm making that up. Certainly, Pozzo always wanted an attacking centre-half cast in his mould, a maker of long passes rather than some snake-hipped ball-carrier, and it was his conversations with Roberts that laid the basis of Pozzo's no-nonsense approach to the game.

*   *   *

Two or three years passed (Beveridge published *Unemployment*, Dr Crippen was hanged, Scott sailed for Antarctica, Saussure completed his *Cours de linguistique générale* . . .) and Pozzo's family finally lured him home (to attend his sister's wedding which he couldn't really avoid anyway) and in a crisis on the eve of the 1912 Stockholm Olympiad, he was appointed Italian team manager for the first time. Although his hastily assembled side was beaten 5–1 by Austria, improvement was forthcoming as Pozzo (assisted by the pragmatic coaching of the former Manchester United professional Billy Garbutt) added discipline, stamina, work-rate, organization, speed, commitment, discipline, stamina, work-rate, organization, speed, commitment and phlegm to the natural Latin skill, *brio* and suchlike. By the early 1920s, Italian football was amongst the best in Europe . . .

CHAPTER IV

REEFER MADNESS

But back to 1934. Pozzo was now in his second run in command. Italy's opponents in the semi-final were Austria, survivors of a fractious quarter-final with their neighbours Hungary and managed by Pozzo's great rival Hugo Meisl. Playing the passéist Scottish-passing game long since abandoned by the British, the Austrian so-called *Wunderteam* (mostly epicene college boys who enjoyed poncing about making pretty little triangles) had in recent years put together a series of relatively impressive results, notably a narrow 4–3 defeat by England at Stamford Bridge in 1932.

The night before the semi-final, Pozzo knocked on my door.

'I have two words to say to you, Olivia.'

'*Two*? Are you okay?'

He sounded okay.

'*I'm* okay.'

'Stay there.'

I stubbed out my cigarette, set aside my heavily annotated copy of *Miss Lonelyhearts* (really, he could do worse than despair), lowered the lamps, douched, threw on a white silk wrap with a white fur collar, re-painted my somewhat thin and pallid lips, flung open the door, and ushered him in.

'That's a slinky outfit, Olivia.'

'Such beautiful silk it's almost see-through.'

'*Almost*.'

'You said *two* words, Signor.'

He wandered over to the dresser, opened it, and found a bottle of *grappa*. He said:

'Does the name Matthias Sindelar mean anything to you?'

I wandered over to the dresser and closed it.

'Excuse me. What was the question?'

'Does the name Matthias Sindelar mean anything to you?'

'*Sindelar*? Um . . . let's think . . . Shesternev . . . Simonian . . . Simonsson . . . Simpson . . . ah! Sindelar, Matthias: the tall, slender, self-aware, solvent ball-wizard, star of the Austrian *Wunderteam*. Height: 6′ 1″. Weight: 9st 3lbs, *sans erection*. Married: not yet. Car: 1931 Pontiac saloon. Known to his family, friends and many lovers as "Motzl", but to the football world as *der Papierene* . . .'

'You have done your homework.'

I sat down on the sofa and rolled a cigarette.

'Would you like a drink?'

'Where do you keep the glasses?'

'Over there.'

I lit the cigarette.

*   *   *

At length Pozzo found the glasses, washed them, poured two drinks and handed me one.

'But *der Papierene*? That is difficult to translate into Italian, Olivia. To us he is known as –'

'The Magician.'

Pozzo sat down beside me.

'Why the Magician?'

'If my memory serves me well, Signor, my life was a banquet where every heart . . .'

'I'd better have that.'

I gave him the cigarette.

'If I remember rightly, Signor, at the spanking new Prater Stadium in '32, he conjured both goals out of nothing in Austria's 2–1 victory over Italy. Your team were unable to hold him that day and, finding it all too much to translate *der Papierene*, simply called him thereafter –'

'You can stop there.'

'– yes, Signor . . . the *Magician*. What, with his mazy dribbles, deft little flicks and a shot full of jiggery-pokery, he is, on his day, *spellbinding* frankly. But,' I tapped the side of my nose, 'not tomorrow, Signor. Oh, no. Hm. Did Viktor Shklovsky smoke? *Signor*?'

Pozzo shook his head. I drained my drink, and poured two more . . .

. . . outside the rain lashed against the window pane.

CHAPTER V

SHOWBOAT

The Italians outfought and outran the Austrians on a pudding of a pitch in Milan. With Sindelar slipping and sliding all over the show, the Austrian attack lacked guile and penetration and Guaita scored the only goal of the game, taking a defence-splitting punt from

Monti in his stride before firing low and hard past the cowering Hiden.

CHAPTER VI

LITTLE CAESAR

June 10, 1934. Only Czechoslovakia stood beteween Italy and the glittering Jules Rimet Trophy . . .

There had been a strong tradition of fancy football in Prague since a Scottish international, John Dick, had gone there to coach in, say, 1904 . . . I'm not absolutely sure. But never mind that . . .

Steel-helmeted troops lined the quaint little Stadio Torino in Rome . . . Fascist flags hung limply in the gentle breeze . . . the military band played the best of Gregor and his Gregorians . . . and five minutes before kick-off, Mussolini made his entrance.

A brooding silence descended on the arena.

Ravens wheeled in the cloudless sky.

There was a single, strangulated cry of 'Tosser' and *Il Duce* squeezed into his seat with a moue. Down in the touch-line dug-out, Pozzo sat hunched, scribbling post-match ripostes in a ragged old copybook:

'Signor Pozzo, at a time when the dictators are seeking prestige, how important is victory, psychologically, for Mussolini in the struggle for Axis leadership?'

'I refuse to mix soccer with politics.'

'Wrong answer. Listen carefully, Signor. At a time when the dictators are seeking prestige, how important is victory, psychologically, for Mussolini in the struggle for Axis leadership?'

'Very psychological. Now if you'll excuse me I think I'll join the boys in the bath.'

'*Thank you, Signor. And congratulations.*'

CHAPTER VII

TRIUMPH OF THE WILL

The final was a nice and tight affair until the seventieth minute, when Puc beat the unsighted Combi to put the Czechs ahead. Disaster loomed. Just eight minutes remained when Orsi collected a raking pass from Ferraris on the edge of the area, shrugged off challenges from Kostalek and Zenisek, spotted Planicka off his line, feinted with his left foot, before unleashing a steepling donkey-drop with his weaker right. It cleared the clutching fingers of the back-pedalling Planicka, plummeted under the bar and sent the match into extra-time. Pozzo ordered Meazza and Ferrari to sit back in midfield, and the exhausted Schiavio to switch with Guaita every two or three minutes. After the second switch, Guaita slipped a slide-rule pass through a square Czech defence. The big centre-forward, mustering the strength of desperation, timed his run to perfection and his first-time shot flashed inside the near post. Planicka didn't smell it. The Azzurri shut up shop, the final whistle blew, and Mussolini presented Combi with the Cup.

CHAPTER VIII

WOMAN TO WOMAN

That evening, flushed with reflected glory, I wiggled down Viale Trastevere to Attilio's bar. Tacked to the door was a notice which read:

PRIVATE FUNCTION
PLAYERS' WIVES 7–8 P.M.
SWEETHEARTS 8 TILL LATE

I knocked, waited, listened, heard nothing. I was about to leave when a *vollbusig* blonde came to the door. She gave me a quick once-over and purred:

'Oh, boy! And who are *you*?'

'Peppino's fuckbird.'

'Pretty name,' she cooed, taking my hand in hers, and patting it with the other. 'I'm his wife. Here, I thought you'd like this.'

His wife? His *wife*? But, hey, I was too much of a woman for any one man. I turned and ran down the street and hailed a cab.

To the *Taverno Metodo*, driver. *Pronto*!'

'Ah, Inglesi! But I know it! Hop in. Mmm, nice pair of pins, lady.'

I smiled sweetly, and not until the taxi was squeaking down the street did I realize that my fingers were clutching a World Cup winner's medal!

And I was meeting Matthias Sindelar for dinner . . .

CODA

Vittorio Pozzo retired in 1948; his last match in charge was Italy's 4–0 home defeat by England (Stan Mortensen, Tommy Lawton, Sir Tom Finney 2). He later became a journalist with La Stampa, *for whom he wrote until his death in 1969.*

Giuseppe Meazza (with Giovanni Ferrara, the sole survivors from the 1934 side) captained Italy to a second successive victory in France in 1938. He was to score a record 33 goals for his country in 53 appearances.

Matthias Sindelar died soon after his retirement in 1939. He was 35.

About 'Olivia', what can I say? Whenever I flick through her memoir of Italia 34, *I think, Grandma (a pint-sized factory girl from the back streets of Manchester), what were you on?*

Sources

World Soccer from A to Z edited by Norman Barrett (London: Pan Books Ltd, 1973)

The Puffin Book of Football by Brian Glanville (Harmondsworth, Middlesex: Penguin Books Ltd, 1970)
Dramas of the World Cup by Patrick Greene (London: City Magazines Ltd, 1966)

The Slap of a Frido Five Size

Peterjon Cresswell

Time stands still for sport's greatest moments, as if giving us mere mortals the chance to capture their beauty and register their significance. That freeze-frame of Bob Beamon's face twisted in mid-air disbelief during his legendary long jump or the classic image of a young Cassius Clay impudently dancing around a defeated Sonny Liston for his first heavyweight title would both be prime contenders.

My moment took place during the World Cup of 1970. Like a first kiss haunting every subsequent love affair, it plays a constant internally programmed video loop, recurring every four years like some benevolent malarial angel, her wand waving the projectionist into action every mid-morning of every first day of every tournament ever since.

With the headrush of the first celebratory drink in the month of excess to follow, it comes alive. It is late in the game, in fact the final game. Brazil-Italy, 3-1 the scoreline. The fortnight's foreplay we can both share later, but for this one moment in time, Pelé has the ball and is considering his options while his Italian opponents stand off in trepidation. It is a defence which has spent most of its destructive lifespan breaking down Europe's best in its *catenaccio* approach to international club competition, but we're not in Europe now, we're in Mexico, and this movie is mine, it's my generation's, it's Brazil's and it's Pelé's. With no hint of a quick glance back or shout of a familiar nickname, Pelé nonchalantly lays off a ball to his right, of a pace, balance and length as precise as the technology which was then sending astronauts to the moon. But to whom? For that split second, even now, and every World Cup morning ever after, neither

I, nor the Italian defence, nor half the world watching on TV can anticipate Carlos Alberto's blind-side run down the right touchline. The Brazil team captain meets Pelé's ball perfectly, hitting it over 20 yards out at a height normally occupied by Flymo mowers and at a speed heightened by the rarefied atmosphere of the Aztec stadium's elevated altitude. It crashes into the corner of the net with a righteous climactic force that earns Carlos Alberto sporting immortality and minutes later thrusts the World Cup into Brazil's hands for ever. Jules Rimet, his name on the original trophy won for the third and final time by a Brazil of rare skill and adventure, could rest in blissful peace. With this final goal of his competition, the World Cup's visionary administrator's will and testament had been well and truly served.

This winter in Budapest I met its executor. Carlos Alberto, balding, smiling and even podgier in a spacehopper-shaped hooped football top, strode out as the star guest of a gala five-a-side show tournament. People my age rose as one around me, all basking in the reflected glory of that shared moment in time, in Budapest as it was in heaven. Hungary, rich in World Cup legend, still recognises its duty to the beautiful game. After shuffling around his own half for all of three minutes, O Capitao directed operations from the bench with a dignity he kept when swamped by autograph-hunters afterwards. I saved my moment for after the press conference.

With an English perfected with Pelé's at New York Cosmos and a politeness reserved for the same question constantly asked of him over three decades, Carlos Alberto talked me through his moment. 'It was without doubt the most beautiful and most important shot of my life,' he beamed. I am listening to a man who will die peacefully satisfied, I thought. 'But you cannot imagine what a lucky shot it was! Look at the video film if you have one.' (I gave a mysterious smile.) 'When Pelé stuck that little pass out to the right to me, the ball gave a little jump on a bump in the turf you could hardly see. Despite that, it was my good fortune to hit the ball!'

A bump in the turf! Did Beamon's run-up strike a loose bit of gravel, Ali's glove avoid a stray mosquito?

There was no time to reflect on this as Carlos Alberto offered a quick handshake and a gesture indicating his necessity to offer his complete attention to the clamour of similar questions all around him. I threw him back a nod and smile of thanks and recognition of his obligations as the guardian of one of football's most cherished memories. I couldn't hear if his answers were wavering from the ones captured in my dictaphone, because I was happily drowning in another noise which was pulling me back over to the empty arena, conveniently of similar dimension to where the noise was coming from . . .

Dust is being scuffed up by the keen activity of two dozen shoes shuffling over Grovelands Primary School playground. 'G'wan score!' is the shout I hear above all the others, George Medford having slipped me a dream pass, and I slap my instep against the dimples of the half-bright orange Frido Five Size football being scrapped over all playtime, all summer long in fact. English schoolboys had been scrapping over a football for 150 years, leaving it to men like Rimet to run with it, but this felt different, to me at least. Football wasn't the same any more.

All spring we had been collecting sticker cards, not of mundane, muddied stars of the First Division All Stars, but of bright Peruvians with red sashes, tracksuited Czechoslovaks with exotic surnames, and a team called El Salvador. El Salvador! What was an El Salvador? Was it fruit flavoured? Was it something you should tell the nit nurse about?

'Good Morning Mexico', fuzzy-coloured and husky-voiced over the satellite link-up, revealed all. Every morning, wolfing down our cereals, we were transfixed to the TV screen, rushing into school to play out Pelé, Rivelino and Jairzinho. We were absolute beginners, innocents at home, with no concept of how rare it all was, just an intuitive appreciation of what the game could be.

Instead of the usual headless charge, options opened up, dream passes exchanged, space made, angles created. It seemed all so simple, that football was brain-over-brawn, a variety of options, the sea of possibility in the forward pass. All it needed was someone like a Pelé, or a George Medford, to open it all up . . . for years the beauty of their passing disguised for me a perhaps more significant factor: their colour.

Why, if the best kids in the school playground, the best Olympians, Beamon and Clay, and the best Brazilians were black, why were all the faces stuck into my First Division All Stars album firmly white? Why would our subsequent Secondary School 1st XI be made up of dour, white battlers shouted at by touchline parents and some results-obsessed games master alike? Why did the 1970 World Cup then assume some mythological loss of face due to that fatal glass of beer instead of triumphing the glorious football fantasy it really was? What happened to the simple things in life?

In truth, simple was only that simple to someone of that age, born late '58, as beautifully significant to us as all of our totems. The first cut is the deepest, and our teeth were cut on Brazilian football, T Rex singles, Bowie albums, Clash tours, and make next year's marketing men happy, why don't you, by filling in the rest yourselves.

Hindsight and worse, foresight, tell a story of magic and loss.

A late-comer debutant to the 1958 ball, and an injured party to the dour, defensive, disappointing versions in 1962 and 1966, Pelé knew he had to make the 1970 World Cup Finals his own. Too old to shine as significantly in 1974, having rejected the pressurised riches of European club football, achieved his 1,000th goal and made enough noise to have national coach Joao Saldanha replaced by the more malleable Mario Zagallo, Pelé seized his moment. Neither of his two strokes of genius – his centre-circle chip against Czechoslovakia or his outrageous dummy against Uruguay – resulted in a goal, so he would slip that dream pass for his captain to finish the job instead. Team-mates at Santos, Pelé and Carlos Alberto would have been playing matches at city, state, national and international level every two days, all year round, for close to a decade.

1970 was the last innocent World Cup. It was the last in the traditional four-group, straight-knockout format. It featured no sendings-off, no ugly scenes with referees, no penalty dives, no time-wasting substitutions and no Argentinians.

It was the first modern World Cup. It was the first to be driven by economics, matches played at high noon to satisfy the European media. It was the first to allow substitutions, used sparingly and occasionally brilliantly, the first to generate package trips from England, pop songs in the charts and coin collections from local garages. It was the first screened in televised colour, displaying that Brazilian gold which would entice frissons of anticipation at every World Cup since.

Yet all that's left of this dream I hold is just that, a band of gold.

No one settling down to the 1994 World Cup Final was expecting that unexpected chip, dummy or dream pass. Mario Zagallo once risked all on tactically restraining Gerson for an entire half before throwing his chain-smoking midfield genius at the Italian front, holding Brazil to 1-1 at half-time; now his Brazil was part of the whole fantasy-free football package, World Cups won or lost on weary defensive error or on the contrived drama of penalties.

1998 is coming back to haunt me already. Paris or Peckham, it's all the same. That fatal sip of beer has time on its side, Pelé over the ball and Carlos Alberto waiting in the wings.

The morning after, me and George Medford will ball the wall, he Pelé, me Carlos Alberto, the slap of a Frido Five Size going THAKAFUCKAFUCKATHAKAFUCK against the playground walls until long after the primary school gates have been closed.

Gary Sobers

Tim Lawler

If we had we a one a him we'd see us a home an a dry ina France a'right. If we ca field a de West Indies fi soccer like in a de cricket den evry lickle ting gwan be irie, nuh lie.

Sorry, didn't mean to startle. Go back to sleep. Doze right back off. Go on. I'll be here, sitting quietly.

Sittin' here under this tree. And this loneliness won't set-uh me free. One hundred miles I roam just to make this trunk my home. Ooh I'm just . . .

It's just . . . no. Sorry. Ssshh.

Beer? No. Mind if I . . .?

It's just that's how you have to talk to Jamaicans, that's all. Irie an' ting an' dat. No I can see you're not, can see that, obviously, with your suncream and everything, but Dennis is. He's Jamaican, and he's due here soon, and I was practising. That sort of talk doesn't come easy to an educated man such as I (and I, et cetera), but hey. One love.

One Love is what Deon Thingy from Luton or Derby or somesuch tepid outfit said to the Jamaican press when he scored against Costa Rica or some other tinpot spot in a de qualifiers back in '97. That's what Dennis said, how he won them over from tinking him some Jimmy come-lately over from a Inglan all full of heself and never take a bowl of cornmeal porridge ina him life much less the guvernmen lodge in Trenchtown and he only won them over, innit, just by saying One Love instead of One Nil and mixing up his channels and that's about how easy it is to succeed in Jamaica.

Only I'm not Jamaican, as I hope you could probably tell. I'm Barbadian, and all this had rather passed me by. I learned it from the Jamaican fellow called Dennis I met last night under this very tree or *arbre* by this *rond-point* outside the *hypermarché* and taking a drink or thirty-one to wile away the time and are you sure? I've got loads.

That's more or less exactly as he said it, like that up there. *If we had we a one a him we'd see us a home an dry ina France a'right. If we ca field a de West Indies fi soccer like in a de cricket den evry lickle ting gwan be irie, nuh lie.*

Now correct me if I'm wrong but when I last took a real read-all-about-it interest in boys' sports – and in those days it really was *read* rather than *hear* – Derby belonged to Brian Clough and I'm sure Luton were something to do with Morecambe and Wise. Where does Gary Sobers fit into that, then? Different league, Denn my frien'. Imagine a team of Charlie Georges and Ray MacFarlands and whoever the fuck played for Luton before Thingy Stein and some footballing equivalent of Gary Sobers, some latterday Compton figure, only black, all in the same side. If we had one of him we'd still be Derby and Luton with Cruyff at his peak spraying passes into empty space. Nice of Dennis to humour me by remembering a Barbadian colossus, an Achilles among Patrocli, but honestly.

In the Clough, George and Wise days, Gary was still turning out for Northants every now and again but I seem to have been a bit preoccupied since then. I can still remember how to say preoccupied but I sure as hell can't spell it no more. Any more. But I usually manage to keep a grip. Are you sure I can't tempt you? Mind if I do?

Sorry sorry sorry that only happens when you shake them up should be more careful how I carrythem nexttime. No don't go, really. Stay. No more singing. No . . .

It's just there's a slow song going through my head as I sit and wait and watch the world arrive in France and learn French words. It goes My Island, Don't Sell Out. It's by someone called Burning Spear, apparently, and Dennis was playing it earlier, and he means Jamaica. That's their island, Dennis's and Burning's, only Burning says Hisland with an H as in *My Highlan'* because he's being all Jamaican irie innit et cetera. Seen?

And we don't have to sell out, do we, says Dennis, and he's right. Don't have to shout for Nigeria because they're black nor France for Viera the celebrated Martiniquan nor yet Inglan because Incey's old man came from Grenada or Antigua or wherever. I just made all those up because I can't remember too clearly exaclty what he said or whose ancestors came from where but that was the giSt. How they can say *Regardez! Je et je viens en un France righteousement stylée* because that's where they've come, come to invade the Old World right back, them with their dreads and their irie and everything. I'm beginning to think that's what Mike at work meant too. He meant Jamaica. But he didn't *say* Jamaica, did he?

He said Barbados, and that's where all my troubles started, the like of which nobody knows but, erm, Jesus, I think. I'm almost sure that's how it goes.

Look, I have many rivers to cross but for the life of me can't seem to find my way over the first one, having as they do no rivers at all in Barbados, but let's see if there's any life left in this old ford. Bear with me. Can see you not asleep so I'll carry on until you tell me to stoP.

Ahem.

My name is Eddy (as in Grant) Banks (as in Gordon) and also, and far more relevant to my current situation, as in Barbados's only brewery. The reason it's more relevant to that is first because I'm a bit drunk and second because unlike Gordon I'm not saving a blessed thing in fact rather its opposite and second because I'm a bit, um, drunk. But there's a message in all dem bottles, and it goes a little . . . like this.

I have an excellent job in England where I live and where I was born and was once, as you can probably tell, educated. I lift crates of paint onto palettes and stack them all neatly for the forklifts so they won't unbalance and leave impromptu Jackson Pollocks all over the floor of the factory store. Not the class of metier my education might have led me to expect but then I didn't expect to be spending so much time in the open wards of the Maudsley Hospital either.

The questions started way back in Clapham Park Infants but went away when I was nine as we thought forever. Then I had one last large visit from whatever patient demon stowed away on the boat with dad and I can't really read much any more. But I remember everything.

No stay. please. I'll try to sit still.

There. Well that's fine. I'll remember anyway.

Back less far, around seven months ago now, Mike and Carl are sitting around messing at tea break time and they can see me and the other young bucks playing soccer in the yard and it's November in Camberwell and it's freezing so I run around a lot and in consequence score a smashing goal from all of several yards and without thinking raise my arm and at the end of the arm there's a fist.

Something to do with the weather, I think, like less hand to get cold stuck up there in the air than if all the fingers were all stuck out, or something. I usually turn out to have had *something* on my mind.

And Carl calls over What's this, Black Power? What are you, Malcolm bleedin X or summink and Mike says Malcolm Tent more like and Carl says Eh? and then Mike says Mind you, them Barbados boys done OK and I stand there my hand still up in the air and say Barbados? See, I remember.

Barbados, says Mike. In the World Cup. Beat Mexico, didn't they. Yesterday.

No they never, says Carl. They only drew but they got through because the other lot lost in Miami. Michigan. Chicago. Somewhere. America anyway and it means your lot are through.

And I want to say What, Palace? What, Clapham Casuals? What, Landor Comprehensive? like Ian Wright would but despite myself I say What, Barbados?

Well we don't mean your Care in the Community brotherhood, do we, say Carl and Mike. We mean Barbados. Your lot.

I must look at the papers more. Or at least acquire the popular habit of having them read to me from the back first. Or get a TV, or stop having these blackouts that see me back in residence sometimes for weeks on end.

After one of those spells the only way of catching up with the world in general is through the guys at the paint factory but they're usually pretty reliable. They kept me up to date with the war against Belgium in '96, for instance, which is why we had to rename the colour Belgian Chocolate as This Year's Black. Even saved the cushy job of relabelling all the tins when I came back to work the time before last. They care about me like that because since my affliction I'm a bit behind, as my mother RIP would say, but then they're supposed to. They're my Community.

They told me all the ins and outs of the OJ case which was just starting when I went in last time and how when he was found guilty they took the *Simpsons* off the BBC in protest and when it came back on, Homer (that's the main character) was white. Or was it innocent? Anyway they kept me informed about all that and this time they've been telling me all about Barbados and the Road To France and it seems I've been missing some rare times.

I hadn't even been aware they'd been in it, except as I imagined in a pre-pre-tournament the like of which gets all the Faroe Islands and Vaticans out of the way early and you never read about in papers unless you live there, which I don't, never having set foot on the island land of my forefathers despite knowing all about the rivers or lack of them from my mum and the brewery from my dad and of course from my name.

But apparently not. It seems Barbados have been taking on places with cities bigger than my hisland and giving a more than respectable account of themselves. It appears they drew with Mexico and the USA (the USA!), beat Costa Rica and Canada and all sorts and are even now here in France as I myself am.

Only I can't find them anywhere. I've saved and saved since

November and taken my first real holiday that doesn't involve hard beds and male nurses and come here to Boulogne and there seems to be no mention.

I know I could have got all the way to Paris from Waterloo but One it was all booked and Two it's a sight cheaper on the ferry and I thought I'd hitch a lift with some 'bados supporters soon as I got here but there were none on the boat and I've yet to meet any in Boulogne, but I have met Dennis and he's Jamaican so that's halfway there. I mean as he himself says if we had a West Indies team like we do in cricket we'd be supporting the same side and Barbados would have had at least a couple fellows in, like Sir Garfield.

Says Dennis, but that shows how much he knows. A couple? We've always had at least three since the days of Walcott, Weekes and Worrell, the 3 Ws who have roundabouts named after them that light up all through November every year in honour of Independence. At night, anyway. No sense in throwing money away as my dad RIP would say, and as I'd say too if I'd ever been and seen them all lit up in the bright Caribbean sunshine. But beer isn't throwing it away, is it, especially not at hypermarket prices where Red Stripe is just 42 francs for six.

I bought six Red Stripes in honour of Dennis and as a mark of respect and as they didn't have Banks or even Carib but what do you expect when the Trinnies aren't even here well what do you expect from a country that needs two islands to make a nation and still can only muster Brian Lara I mean honestly.

There wasn't only Red Stripe. There was a huge France '98 palette stacked (reasonably competently, as far as I could tell) with beer from all the different countries, right in the front of the store. I can still do short words when it really matters and up really close and can recognise labels and they had Becks, 1664, Stella, San Msomething, an Italian one called Peron, an easy one called S-O-L, some Argentinian stuff or other with a flag on and probably some Brazilian in its turn, John Smiths, that Sapro or what is it with the Japanese writing, amateur Eastern brews with tigers and lions all over them, ditto with fjords and mermaids and moustachioed deities from our friends in the north, that Scottish one with the girls, two sorts of Bud and some nice bottled water for the Saudis and Iranians.

But no Banks with the pirate ship on it. So anyway I bought some of each and only have the Red Stripe left and if Dennis doesn't hurry along soon I won't vouch for its prospects. But that's Jamaicans all over, *n'est-ce pas?* When they reach, they reach.

Let me just go over what Mike said again. Hold on, here's a Belgian.

Phew, that was close. Right. Mike said Your lot are through and I said What Barbados and he said That's right, your lot. Now IF I'd said What, the West Indies? and he'd said Well one of them anyway but I'm not sure I remember which one, Barbados, was it, or Jamaica or what's that other one, Tobago?, and if Carl had chipped in Antigua I think that's one of theirs and is it Gambia? Mozambique? they all sound alike to me, then I might have begun to suspect they'd got it wrong and I would have checked. Bought my own paper and checked. Had someone read it to me and checked.

But it wasn't like that at all. It was there on the back of Mike's *Daily Mirror*, Barbados Make History. I didn't see but they said. Peter read it out to me and that's what it said. And then an article about how we were the first English-speaking Caribbean nation to qualify ever and how the PM had granted all the team plots of land to build on when they came home, triumphant or not, and how the world has dubbed them the Calypso Boyz. He wouldn't let me actually hold the paper myself because I was supposed to be busy and as he says I can't read for coconuts and he is the foreman but he shouted it across the yard and he said it said Barbados Make History so it can't be Mike and Carl letting me down. Besides it's been over six months now and they've said something about it every day since, so they can't have got it wrong or they'd have said something. They read the papers *every* day. They've all got *big* TVs.

They even gave me a lift to Victoria and seemed delighted I was going, all smiles and laughter and they wouldn't have been like that if they weren't sure. Even bought me some food for the journey. Bananas, a whole great big bunch of them, and took my picture holding them and my mum's old BWI Airlines bag to show the guys at work, here's Slow Eddy off to France to watch Barbados.

But I'm still sat here under my tree next to the big roundabout and there's no sign, no flag with a broken trident among the many flags waving outside the hypermarket and no Banks beer on the palette inside. Perhaps they think we all drink Red Stripe. That it all tastes alike.

Gary Sobers has a roundabout name after him too, and a gymnasium, and they're all called the Sir Garfield this and that and t'inking of him reminds me of one of the first football facts I ever learned, nameLy that the highest score ever in the first-class game was when Arbroath beat Brechin City 36-0 and I thought of Gary way back then. That's exactly as many points as six sixes in an over, like what only Gary Sobers has ever hit, so you see it *can* be done in a de football too.

If we had us a one of him we'd be fine. Really. If we could all play for the same side. Then we'd show 'em, boy. Then.

But look, haH, what I tell you, seen – somet'ing dreadlocked this way comes and look, it is, it's Dennis, Dennis and three tea-cosied pals and that's about how many Red Stripes I have left. I'd been looking at them and thinking it's a shame about Peru but now here's Dennis and listen he's calling me brother and he's glad I'm still here and would I like to come along with them to watch Jamaica? Well yes I would. Yes Dennis yes if you ca just help me get up. Stand up. Stand up fi mi right.

Because after all if we should can field a West Indies side like we can in cricket we'd be supporting the same side. We'd be home an a dry and have roundabouts back home name after us and we wouldn't sit around under trees like drunks, no sir.

We'd be like sobers.

Maradona: USA '94

David Baddiel

Some days, I really hanker after the idea of the best player in the world. It's not *clear* any more. Who is it now? Ronaldo? Too young, too unproven and too like a chipmunk. Maldini? Well, his best appearance in football's last major competition was on a Reebok poster. George Weah? When's he ever going to be judged at international level playing for Liberia? Gazza? Could have been, perhaps, if only Roger Milford had booked him for that first tackle. Francis Benali? And yet, when I was a kid, it *was* clear: it was Pelé. Then it was Cruyff. And then – without any debate, and don't let anyone tell you any different – it was Maradona.

Young people growing up now probably just think of him as that drug-addict who spooned the ball into the net with his hand against England, but let's be straight about this: *Maradona was the greatest player of his time, and probably the greatest player of all time.* He had more natural ability than Pelé – I'm talking here of course about someone with incredible natural ability being pipped at the post by someone with just one per cent more natural ability – and he played at a time when the game had become considerably quicker, tighter and more bruising.

Which is why I remember taking Maradona's suspension from USA '94 following a positive drugs test so badly. How on earth, I still wonder, did he think he was going to get away with it? 'Oh, they won't test *me*, not with my record'? Or maybe, having heard that it took the dehydrated Tommy Coyne three hours to produce a sample after Ireland vs Italy, he thought he could stall the FIFA officials until they gave up, saying, 'Ah well, Diego, we trust *you* . . .'

I remember how, with hindsight, the much replayed spectacle

of Maradona roaring at the camera after scoring in Argentina's first game against Greece changed its shape. Originally, it seemed incredibly exciting, a shouting from the global rooftops that he was back, that he was still, at 33, eight years on from the Azteca, the greatest player in the world. Afterwards, it became just the ravings of a speed-freak.

When I think about that image now, I wonder why it didn't occur to me at the time that he was on drugs. It must've been blocked out of my mind by footballing hope. Because Maradona, like Paul Gascoigne, was a player you wanted to forgive. Whatever else he did, however often he arched his back as he flipped over like a squat swan in search of another free-kick, all that melted into the ether when he suddenly decided to play his football, football which he seems to have learnt in another world. When he played that way, it was like standing in a blinding light in which it became impossible any more to see him punching the ball over Peter Shilton's head or blubbering like a three-year-old as Lothar Matthäus raises the trophy. I really wanted to be blinded by that light.

And it was a comeback; nothing raises the emotions in sport like a good comeback. Ali winning his third title at 36, Martina Navratilova winning through to her twelfth Wimbledon final at 38 – there is something about an old stager returning to the fray in their twilight years and announcing *I'm still the best* that's guaranteed to stiffen the goose pimples all down the arms. It's something to do with seeing age, death and young pretenders thwarted; with seeing cynics have their *schadenfreude* snatched from them. Maradona at USA '94 was looking to be one of these, the last act of a huge human drama – and then it wasn't.

The really irritating thing about the whole story was the sneaking suspicion that drugs would've made no difference to Maradona's performance at all. I've had asthma in the past; I don't remember blowing in some Beconase and suddenly being able to go past five defenders as if they weren't there. The drug might've given him a bit more pace in the last twenty minutes, but it wouldn't have given him the control he showed against Nigeria or the vision he showed against Greece. I mean, he's probably genuinely *got* asthma; after all, years of cocaine don't do the lungs any good. But I don't think it was a considered decision. Maradona didn't take the drug because, after weighing up the dangers, he felt it would add enough to his game to be worth the risk; he took it because, like a big kid, he couldn't resist the temptation, and because he thought he could get away with it.

I felt more let down than I should; and still now, a strange mixture of loss and annoyance. Perhaps because this last, shabby bit of cheating from Maradona broke the back of a camel that I thought could never be broken, a camel I might call – stretching this camel thing far too far – the footballer's leeway camel. Footballers have this, this *licence*, this ability to behave like complete arseholes and yet still, with one bit of magic, demand my reverence. But Maradona became the first one to be just *too* disappointing. He went too far. I have an image in my head now of Maradona trapping the ball with his heel, or knocking it sideways over his head, or chipping it with backspin, or as Gary Lineker told me he once saw him do in a warm-up before an England vs Rest of the World XI, kicking it straight up twenty foot in the air over and over again, and then turning to me with a pleading, conciliatory look, and me just thinking, oh sod off. Leave me alone.

Back Home

Colin Shindler

It was a job I had been postponing for weeks, ever since we sold the house and knew we had to clear out by the end of June. I don't know why I was dreading it so much. Maybe it was just the hard work. I'd shifted the stuff from the loft in the pre-war semi which was our first house and I'd hated it, particularly the moment when I had to transfer my weight from the floor of the loft to the top of the stepladder. Fifteen years later I knew that I had accumulated far more stuff and the whole process of shifting those cardboard boxes had to begin all over again.

The moment I saw it I knew what was inside. It was a cardboard box all right but it was covered, for no reason I could readily remember, in a blue sticky formica paper, the sort with which my mother used to line the cutlery drawer of the kitchen table. It had been nearly thirty years since I'd sealed it. It was like those ceremonies they perform at school, burying certain key artefacts of the decade, so that in five hundred years' time future civilisations can look at a videocassette of *Heartbeat* or listen to a CD of the Spice Girls. The fact that they are unlikely to have the inclination to do so never seems to occur to anyone.

Kate had shown no interest in the box, being too embarrassed by her own collection of juvenilia to make enquiries into mine. The kids had gone off to play at their friends' house and Kate had eventually found her car keys where she left them under yesterday's newspaper and driven off to the supermarket in a bad temper. Nevertheless I took the box into the spare bedroom to open. Somehow it felt wrong to open it in the bedroom where our kids had been conceived.

It wasn't that I was ashamed by its contents, simply that they didn't seem to belong in that house. They belonged to a different time. I was a different person. I recognised him as I would recognise a photograph of Jimmy Greaves. Not the *Saint and Greavesie* Jimmy Greaves but the slim, elegant ruthless goalscoring machine in a white Tottenham shirt.

He was past his peak in 1970 was Jimmy. Famously he'd never made it to the World Cup Final in 1966 even though me and most of my mates had wanted him to play up front against West Germany with Geoff Hurst. That's because we were all West Ham fanatics and we hated Roger Hunt who was useless. We could never work out why Alf Ramsey kept picking him. Mind you he picked Martin Peters out of nowhere so he was all right with us was Sir Alf.

There was some other stuff in the box, things which I really had forgotten about. There was a wall chart which I had filled in religiously with all the details of every match played in the Finals, from the opening game at the Azteca Stadium until the unspeakable disaster at Leon. There was also an incomplete collection of Esso coins, silver portraits of the initial squad of forty players which Ramsey announced weeks before the end of the season. It was incomplete because my dad eventually got fed up of having to drive five miles out of his way every time he wanted to fill the car with petrol because I needed an Alan Oakes or a Paul Reaney to complete my collection.

The diary itself was just a school exercise book. I'd been given it just before we broke up for the Easter holidays. Since I was pretty much on constant study leave thereafter, going back into school only for the A level exams themselves, it was conveniently empty when I was looking for something to write in. I didn't set out for it to become a diary. I just wanted something to record my thoughts in. No, that sounds daft. I mean that's what a diary is, isn't it? The point is, I suppose, I never started writing it with the intention that it should become something permanent. I wasn't writing for posterity or anything. I had enough writing to do anyway what with essays on *The Tempest* and The Thirty Years War, neither of which I ever understood. I wrote it out of anger and frustration really but once it was written I couldn't bring myself to throw it away. Like West Ham's relegations these pains inflicted on us become part of us. So it was with the diary.

I haven't got a picture of Julie to remember her by. You'll just have to take it from me that she was like a mixture of Brigitte Bardot and Julie Christie. At any age that's a pretty powerful combination but when you're seventeen years old it's irresistible. She moved in the day after Easter Monday, the last week of March. I first saw her from behind in a pair of tight blue jeans, golden hair spilling half way down her back. She was in the removal van, bending over a packing case. I jammed on the brakes of my Raleigh and skidded into the kerb.

I cautioned myself not to overreact. I was already aware that the rear view of most girls was infinitely more attractive than the front. When she turned round I was going to be really disappointed. She turned round. I wasn't at all disappointed. She looked directly at me and smiled. If she had fired an 88mm shell at me it couldn't have caused greater devastation. With my heart beating like a tom-tom I nonchalantly started to cycle away but put my foot through the chain rather than on the pedal. She didn't see. She was already in the house.

In the space of five seconds I had aged five years. The girls we had fooled around with after school in the park, Alison, Vicki, Carol and that lot, seemed like little kids, still fighting the ravages of acne. This new girl was going to change my life. I knew it instantly. I wasn't wrong exactly, just a little imprecise.

Tuesday 31 March 1970

Don't know what her name is yet but a fab bird moved in at no. 31. Need to find excuse to chat her up. Greaves might just turn out to be fantastic buy. Still don't think Martin Peters is worth £200,000. Spurs will live to rue the day. Home to Wolves tonight and Leeds on Thursday. Ramsey's 28 for Mexico is:

Astle (WBA), Ball (Everton), Banks (Stoke), Bell (Man C), Bonetti (Chelsea), Charlton J. (Leeds), Charlton R. (Man U), Clarke (Leeds), Coates (Burnley), Cooper (Leeds), Hughes (Liverpool), Hunter (Leeds), Hurst (WHU), Kidd (Man U), Labone (Everton), Lee (Man C), Moore (WHU), Mullery (Spurs), Newton (Everton), Osgood (Chelsea), Peters (Traitor), Reaney (Leeds), Sadler (Man U), Shilton (Leicester), Stepney (Man U), Stiles (Man U), Thompson (Liverpool), Wright (Everton). Revised Louis XIV all day.

I had forgotten I had felt so passionately about the transfer that took Martin Peters to White Hart Lane and brought Jimmy Greaves to Upton Park. Greaves was brilliant at first. He never stopped scoring and we picked up three wins and a draw in his first four games. I remember the match against Leeds all right. That was the night Paul Reaney broke his leg in a 2–2 draw at Upton Park. It meant that he missed out on the Cup Final (which Leeds lost) the return leg European Cup semi final against Celtic (which Leeds lost) and the World Cup (too painful to mention).

Leeds played us twenty four hours after a European Cup Semi Final first leg at Celtic. In fact they ended up playing something like 10 matches in 17 days did Leeds. Are you listening, Alex Ferguson? Mind you, they lost nearly all of them which maybe proves Fergie's point. Anyway, Ramsey named Madeley as his replacement for the injured Reaney but Madeley for some reason didn't want to go to Mexico so McNab of the Arse went instead – and came home again when the final squad of 22 was named.

That squad still looks pretty good, better perhaps, like most teams, in retrospect but I remember feeling that it was stronger than the side which had won the Cup in 1966. It's hard now not to recoil when I see the name of Peter Bonetti in that context but Chelsea were a good side that year and won the Cup against Leeds in one of the filthiest matches I have ever seen. Shilton was a kid, not much older than I was, and Stepney was certainly no better than Bonetti. In any case Banks's position was unassailable. Who could possibly have known what was to come?

My mother was surprised when I asked about the new neighbours. She wanted to know whether it was because they had a boy about my age. Did I want to take him to West Ham or something? I said yes because it was easier than owning up to an instant lust for the daughter of the household. In one way I was relieved that my mother hadn't suspected it was the girl who engaged my interest. It was somehow safer to let her continue to believe that my passion for sport disguised any other changes in me. I was going to have to spring directly from schoolboy to married man. Turned out that the kid brother was 14, far too young for me to take to Upton Park. Even Mum saw that.

Mum, of course, through a series of housewifely Chinese whispers, soon found out that the object of my nocturnal emissions was called Julie. The family name was McPherson and her dad was a Scotsman who worked for Ford in Dagenham. Julie was 19 and in her first year at university. All of this was good stuff but I didn't know how it was going to help me make the first move.

Sunday 5 April 1970

Thank God for Carol Vaughan. I wouldn't normally choose to be beaten up by a bird in the middle of Ringway Avenue but her unprovoked attack was a miracle. Don't know why she thought a fumble in the copse near the kids' playground meant anything. Still worked out all right in the end. Going for a coffee with Julie on Tuesday night. Wonder if she's seen Midnight Cowboy *yet? Lost 2–1 at Highbury but Greavesie scored again – with a header for Christ's sake! What a genius! Revised Luther and the Reformation. Hate Luther.*

It was my fault I suppose but I meant it as a joke. I was so obsessed with Julie McPherson that I couldn't think straight. I couldn't revise my European History – that much is clear from the diary – but when Carol showed up at the house claiming I'd stood her up the previous night I pleaded pressure of work. I had a conditional offer of two Bs and a C to read English at

York University and one of three Bs to read English at Bristol so I was keen to do well though I wasn't optimistic about my prospects.

Carol Vaughan was a thickie but compensated for her small intellectual capacity with a pair of tits that were the envy of both sexes throughout the Sixth Form. I'm sorry, that sounds awful, doesn't it, but there's no point in going through this diary if I can't describe exactly how I felt back then. And that is how I felt back then. I don't think I stood her up deliberately but I suppose, walking her back to the bus stop, I shouldn't have said to her pompously, 'Your rival is Miranda'. I meant Prospero's daughter from *The Tempest* but she thought I meant Miranda Williams who was famous for being the town bike.

Anyway Carol clearly wasn't interested in discussing it further because she suddenly clouted me hard across the face with her shoulder bag. As I buried my head in my arm to ward off further blows she kicked me hard in the balls. That one I really felt and slumped to the floor at which point she started putting the boot in like Norman Hunter. Julie heard my cries and came running out of her house. Carol swore at her, then me and then ran away. Julie helped me to a sitting position and offered me a cup of tea. I thought about it for less than a second. It wasn't quite the way I had planned our introduction but it was equally effective.

I was glad to see she made tea the approved student way of smashing one of the new-fangled tea bags into a cup of hot water. It didn't taste as nice as the tea my mother brewed in the pot but I was past caring. I was in. She was amused by my description of myself as a long-suffering Lothario who was subject to random bouts of physical abuse by girlfriends I had jilted. I soon foud out that she was 19 years old, that she was studying Sociology at the University of Essex in nearby Colchester, that she came home frequently to help her Dad because her mother wasn't well and, most wonderful of all, she had dumped her university boyfriend just before they had broken up for Easter. When I suggested, heart pounding, that we went for a cup of coffee in The Golden Egg in the High Street she agreed with an alacrity that set my pulse racing.

Wednesday 8 April

I'm in love for the first time. This is the real thing, not like with Gillian Fern. This is a partnership of equals, intellectual as well as physical, emotional as well as sexual. It's not sexual yet but after the episode towards the end of Midnight Cowboy *it might soon be. Did Goethe's* Faust *today. Went really well. The FA announced that they will be sending out tons of frozen and canned food to Mexico because they don't trust the local food – local cooks more like it. Apparently there's enough kit going out to last a club for a season so presumably they don't trust the washing machines out there either – maybe they don't have washing machines. The Latin Americans obviously hate us. It's a bit of a puzzle because the Argentines and the Uruguayans are well known for being filthy. Why do all the Latin Americans stick together? We wouldn't cross the street if Scotland got a bum refereeing decision. Or the Welsh, or the Irish come to that. Not that there's much chance of any of that lot getting to a World Cup Finals. Maybe it's just Ramsey they hate. He's a cold fish is Sir Alf but he's given us a winning team again. Banks, Moore, Charlton, Hurst, not even Brazil or West Germany can compete with a line-up like that. Everyone's raving about Brazil but they never even got to the quarter-finals last time. I think they're over-rated. I'm sure Pelé's a good player but I've never seen him play a full match and he's old now. This is probably the end of his career and he was injured in '62 and kicked out of it in '66 so what's it all based on? England were unlucky to lose 2–1 to Brazil last summer in the Maracana Stadium. It wasn't even our full squad. I think we'll come home with Bobby clutching that trophy again. The players are getting between £7,000 and £10,000 EACH (including Paul Reaney) from the perks pool. Jesuschristalbleedingmighty!*

I somewhat overestimated the strength of that first date. She hadn't seen *Midnight Cowboy* but I had so I knew which was the best time to get my arm round her shoulder. It was during the scene when Jon Voight is making love on the bed so violently that they are bouncing up and down on the remote control and changing the picture on the television. I knew I could laugh at the sophisticated humour of it all and nonchalantly stretch my arm along the back of her seat before casually slipping it over her shoulder.

The manoeuvre was completed successfully and the gentle opening of her lips at the end of that first good night kiss seemed to me at the time symbolic of future promise. Reading the diary again I don't think I could possibly have foreseen what I was getting into. It's not much consolation but I don't suppose Sir Alf could either. After all he picked the FA Cup winning goalkeeper – not Gary Sprake.

It wasn't only food and kit that the FA were sending out. Everything from medical equipment to studs was going to follow the England team around. We weren't going to lose for lack of preparation. The players in the squad were asked for their favourite authors and books of their choice were to be flown out to ward off the possibility of boredom during the five weeks of preparation before the first match against Romania.

English newspapers were sent in on a daily basis by the journalists. That shows you how long ago it was. Alf was abysmal at public relations, hated the media and still nobody tried to stitch him up. The players talked to journalists back then without reference to their agents. I wonder where that £7,000 to £10,000 perks pool came from. Surely not royalties from the ghastly record 'Back Home'. That was one of the first of the team songs – and one of the worst.

Sunday 12 April

God what a night. We all went round Terry's house to watch the final which Leeds should have won but Sprake threw it away as usual. At least he's out for the replay. Eddie Gray was fantastic. I'd love to see him down Upton Park setting them up for Greavesie. Then we all went on to a party Eddie knew about in Romford. We're in the kitchen trying to grab the drink before it all disappears and I see this amazing looking bird from behind. Reminded me of Julie of course, like all birds do these days. Except that she turns round and it is Julie. I'm stunned for a minute. Is she here with some bloke I wonder? Turns out she went to school with the sister of the bloke who's throwing the party. She gives me this big smile and I know I'm in. 'I'm glad you're here,' she says and grabs my hand. She leads me toward the bedroom. Unbelievable.

My heart is pounding as she leads me upstairs by the hand. I am experiencing a certain amount of discomfort below the waist too as she opens doors looking for an unoccupied bedroom. She pushes me down onto the bed and then perches on my knee, her arms round my neck. I start to try to kiss her greedily but she resists. I want her so badly I'm going to explode. She nuzzles me briefly, lips firmly sealed, then pulls away. 'How do you feel about apartheid in South Africa?' she asks.

Jesus Christ! South Africa?! At a time like that? I'd obviously picked up the wrong signals. On that first meeting we had talked briefly about politics but to be honest I couldn't remember a damn thing I'd said. I suspect I simply agreed with whatever she said and she must have mentioned some left-wing thing and I'd said 'great', which, according to her, made me a member of her Marxist cell.

In April 1970 there was a big campaign run by Peter Hain to stop the tour of England by the South African cricket team which was supposed to start in a few weeks' time. Julie and her leftie friends were dead against it and were planning demonstrations. She wanted me to be part of all that stuff. They were going to sit in the stands behind the bowler's arm and shine mirrors which reflected sunlight into the batsman's eyes.

I told Julie that if she tried that with Eddie Barlow he'd come over and belt her one with his bat. She'd never heard of Eddie Barlow or the Pollock brothers or any of the cricketers of either side. The conversation widened a bit and it turned out she hated cricket which was a bit of a pisser because I was our school captain and she hated football too. Apparently at her university they didn't believe in team games. I thought this was just so much bullshit and said so. You never saw a girl turn that fast. She was off my knee and out of the door in two seconds. My erection disappeared with her.

Wednesday 21 April

England looked OK tonight. They beat Northern Ireland 3–1 with goals by The Traitor, Hursty and Bobby Charlton. Inevitably Best scored for them but avoided getting sent off which he hadn't managed to do against Scotland last Saturday when England were lucky to get away with a 1–1 draw against Wales thanks to one great shot by Lee. You could just about see us doing OK in the World Cup based on tonight's display. Worked on Paradise Lost *and* Antony & Cleopatra. *Can't see why Milton is so great. He just goes on and on. Suppose that's cause he was blind. They never say why he went blind of course. Maybe he . . . No he couldn't. He was a Puritan. You go to hell for a thing like that if you're a Puritan. Saw Julie loading stuff into her dad's new Ford. She's going back to University. I smiled at her. She cut me dead. Bitch! I can't get her out of my mind though.*

The last remark was certainly true enough. Though we disagreed politically, insofar as I had a political viewpoint at all, I had completely lost my cool about the girl. I picked up the newspaper and turned to the front page for a change. There it was – all that stuff about whether the MCC should cancel the tour and the likely response by the anti-apartheid campaigners if they didn't. The more I read the more I started thinking that maybe Julie was right – about this at least.

Saturday 25 April

Really crap 0–0 draw against Scotland at Hampden. 134,000 screaming Jock lunatics and no goals. Serves them right. At least they're not going to Mexico thank God. Will the Jocks ever get to a World Cup? If they couldn't with a team including Law, Crerand and Baxter it makes you wonder if they ever will. England, on the other hand, look good for years to come. There are so many good players coming through though worryingly, apart from Billy Bonds who I really rate, not that many from West Ham. Still today's display was pathetic. I wonder if this is Ramsey's first choice team. They'll have to do better against Romania in the first match. I think I've got the right idea about the Great Reform Bill 1832 now. Piggy Harris was really complimentary about my essay. I just hope it comes up on the day. Saw in the paper that the Foreign Secretary was booed and heckled at the Oxford Union debate. Should I write to Julie in Colchester or just show up there?

Clearly the sexual obsession with Julie was having a profound effect on me. It was as nothing compared with what was to come.

Tuesday 5 May

Four students were killed by soldiers at Kent University in America yesterday. I am really pissed off about this. They were just demonstrating about being drafted, being called up into the army to fight in Vietnam and they got shot. Jesus! It was the sort of demo Julie goes on all the time. I've decided. I'm up to date on my revision. I'm going up to Colchester to see Julie over the weekend.

The diary's a bit sparse after this for a few days so I'll have to fill you in with what I can remember. I got the bus onto the Essex University campus which looked a bit of a shithole to me even though it was almost new. She didn't seem too pleased to see me either at first. She was drinking coffee with another girl and about four or five blokes. When she saw me it was 'Oh hi, this is James' and so on but you wouldn't call it warm exactly. When we left the cafe and started walking back to her room I told her I'd been thinking seriously about what she'd said and her attitude to me suddenly changed. I explained that I had A levels coming up and I couldn't do a lot of demonstrating but she could count me in.

On the way to her room, she grasped my hand firmly in hers. I surreptitiously felt for the outline of the Durex in my jacket pocket but, as usual, I was overestimating the effect of my Damascene conversion or at least her response to it. When we got back to her room it was packed with twenty students all gathered to talk about South Africa and whether they should be banned from the Olympics as well as international cricket.

I still felt a bit pissed off that I wouldn't be able to go and watch Graeme Pollock and Barry Richards after the exams were over but there was a bloke there who knew something about cricket and he said that England would play the Rest of the World in an alternative series of Test matches so that made me much more relaxed.

After the meeting broke up and we'd had a bowl of spaghetti she dropped the bombshell. We were on the bed kissing when I made a frontal attack. She grabbed my hand. 'No,' she said in a voice that brooked no dissension. I looked hurt. She relented a little.

'You want to sleep with me, don't you?'

A rhetorical question if ever I heard one. I nodded.

'What's your last A level?'

'English History 1815–1914.'

'When's that?'

'Thursday 18 June.'

'I'll sleep with you that night. Special treat. If . . .'

'If?'

I couldn't believe there was going to be an 'if'. What sort of 'if' could possibly stop me. At that moment I'd have skied down Everest naked with a carnation up my nose as someone later on said.

'If England have won the World Cup.' And she grinned. Dead evil it was, that grin.

So there it was. The Faustian pact. I had to sell my soul to Sir Alf and the boys. A million thoughts flashed through my brain. Does she know we have to play Brazil in the group matches? Does she know that the games are being played at high altitude? Nobody knew what the effect was going to be. Not till next Friday when we were due to play in Bogota which is 8,600 feet above sea level – nearly 3,000 feet higher than Guadalajara.

'But the final's not till the Sunday – 21 June.'

'I can wait three more days,' she says. 'Can you?'

To tell the truth I wasn't sure if I could.

Wednesday 20 May

The stupid twats at Lord's have announced that the South African tour is to go ahead after all. I find myself really angry about it. Callaghan, the Home Secretary, not the Liverpool winger, is going to intervene. So he bloody well should. The lads have arrived in Bogota. Reports suggest the team spirit is excellent. Thank God. Those lads don't know how much is riding on them. There's going to be a General Election on the 18th June now. I wonder if I can get Julie into bed in the euphoric aftermath of another Tory defeat? The Labour lead over the Tories is 7.5% compared with 3.2% last month. It's going to be a cakewalk for darlin' Harold.

Saturday 23 May

Fabulous results. The main team smashed Colombia 4–0 with two goals by The Traitor, one each by Bobby Charlton and Alan Ball. Even the B side won 1–0 against Colombia B with a scrappy goal by Astle. What's Astle doing out there? I've never rated him. I hope my sex life isn't dependent on Jeff Astle. More important, the South African tour is cancelled today. Those MCC twats had to climb down after all. I feel really good. I left a message at Julie's Hall of Residence. She hasn't rung me back. Is she screwing someone? I'm sick with anxiety. The papers say Don Revie's turned down £100,000 to manage Birmingham for seven years. Well, I don't much care for Revie or Leeds come to that but you've got to admire the bloke's principles. He's clearly not that interested in money.

Sunday 24 May

Julie rings back. She was out with some girlfriends last night. Ha! A likely story! But she's really warm on the phone, thrilled about the South African tour. Now she's talking about the General Election. I tell her, mischievously, that England beat Ecuador 2–0 in a friendly with goals by Francis Lee and Brian Kidd. She laughs and says that sounds like good news for me. Why is it good news for me and not for her? It's worrying is that. Meanwhile Alf is quietly confident. And so am I. He's dropped Shilton, Thompson, Sadler, McNab, Coates and Kidd from the final pool of 22. Looks OK to me.

Tuesday 26 May

No! Disaster!! Bobby Moore has been arrested. I can't believe it. Everyone is stunned. The whole country is shocked. It's those bastard Argentines. They've never forgiven us for getting Rattin sent off at Wembley in '66. It's a plot, a frame-up, obviously. How can anyone take it seriously. It's not helping England team morale though and it's shattered all my dreams. Come on, Moore-o, hang in there, baby!

Wednesday 27 May

There's a hilarious picture of Jeff Astle asleep on an airport baggage trolley looking bombed out of his skull. Is he on dope or something? Apparently he gets air sick. From the look of him he'll never play for England which is probably a bit of a relief. First exam is approaching. First England vs Romania, then German Oral. Can't say that without thinking of Julie.

Thursday 28 May

It's getting worse. They now say Bobby Moore stole a £600 bracelet from a jeweller's shop in Bogota and he'll have to stand trial. It's such a frame-up: Harold Wilson's involved now. They've got to get Bobby back soon. The first game's only five days away. The papers are saying Bobby won't be released in time. My worry is even if he is released in time what sort of a state will he be in?

Friday 29 May

Bobby Moore provisionally released to fly to Mexico today. He's lost seven pounds in weight during his time in custody. We were talking about it at school. We think (hope) that the team will benefit from the incident in Bogota. The more the Latin Americans hate us, the stronger it binds the side together. Maybe. Bastards!

Tuesday 2 June

Can't sleep. England 1 Romania 0. 11pm start. Hurst scored after 64 minutes. The Romanians were filthy. The tackle that put Newton out of the game was a disgrace. We had all the possession but we looked like we'd never score. Lee hit the post, but then Dembrowski missed a sitter. Could so easily have been 0–1. Finally, Ball and Charlton combined to set up Hurst who lost his marker and shot into the far corner. Yes! Hope Julie was watching. German Oral 11.30 tomorrow.

Wednesday 3 June

Oral went all right. Managed to turn conversation onto football and talked about German football team being very good and how we were lucky to win in '66 and let's hope we don't meet till the final this year. Fortunately I'd rehearsed all the key vocab. Brazil smashed Czecho 4–1. The Czechs went ahead but Brazil woke up and scored through Jairzinho (2), Rivelino and Pelé. I now see why everyone raves about Pelé. For me the star was Gerson. Wonder if Ron Greenwood was watching. Fancy him at Upton Park. Italy scraped past Sweden 1–0 and W Germany lucky to beat Morocco 2–1. England or Brazil to win the Cup. Got to be. Chaucer paper on Friday.

I was into the thick of A levels by this time and the diary falls blank again for a few days. I even miss out that amazing match against Brazil on Sunday 7 June. We lost 1–0 but somehow I felt better at the end of it than I did after we'd beaten Romania. The altitude and the heat were still a problem – the England players reportedly each lost 10lbs in weight over the ninety minutes. I'll never forget that Banks save, particularly as they repeat it now so often on TV, or Jair's goal, or Bobby Moore's great tackles, or Lee being booked for kicking their goalie on the head. I thought Mullery was outstanding. The only time he left Pelé's side all night was when they scored. My main memory though is of Pelé and Moore exchanging shirts at the end – two giants of the game behaving like real gents.

Tuesday 9 June

The German Literature was an absolute bastard. I hated Goethe but I thought I could cope. Sadly mistaken. My mind's half on the football, half on Julie and not at all on the exam. I still think we'll meet Brazil again in the Final. We've got to if I'm going to get anywhere with Julie. I just pray to God that Jeff Astle won't be playing. I can't bear to think about that sitter he missed. Alf should have kept Lee on. And I'm not sure he should have taken Charlton off to bring Bell on either. I feel like a nervous wreck. Can't sleep now for worry. It must be like the England team. Apparently the Mexicans invaded the hotel before the Brazil match and sounded hooters all night to keep them awake. They don't have to do a Shakespeare paper tomorrow either.

To my surprise the Shakespeare paper was great. All the questions I'd prepared came up. Then came the match against Czechoslovakia. Ramsey took something of a gamble by resting key players for the quarter-final on Sunday. In the end it was a scrappy performance with only Clarke's goal from a penalty separating the two sides. Meanwhile Germany had beaten Bulgaria 5–2 and it was looking ominous for the crunch match.

The strain was beginning to tell on me. The exams, the general election, would Julie keep her word, had she already found a new boyfriend this term, would we beat Germany again? I dreaded turning over the page to the next entry. I still feel so sorry for myself.

Sunday 14 June

It's over and I'm in shock.

I can't read any more. I even remember where I was sitting when I was writing that entry. Maybe it wouldn't have hurt so much if we hadn't started so brightly. The only change from what we all knew was Ramsey's preferred eleven was Bonetti for Banks who had stomach poisoning but appeared to have recovered on the Saturday night. The return of Banks's illness didn't seem exactly relevant at the time. We hoped his replacement wouldn't be called on much but he was a competent enough keeper. Ha!

At the start you could see the Germans panicking like crazy every time Hurst got the ball – clearly the memory of Wembley '66 was as vivid in West Germany as it was here. The first goal came just past the half hour. Mullery to Cooper to Lee to Newton and Mullery finished it off. 1–0 at half time and I was feeling pretty damn smug. I was even smugger five minutes into the second half when Hurst controlled the ball and slipped it out wide for Newton, overlapping down the right. His cross was met at the far post by ex Hammer Martin Peters who beat Vogts before slipping it past Sepp Maier and that was it. I couldn't remember a time when England had conceded a two goal lead. It was going to be Italy or Mexico in the semis then presumably Brazil in the final though I wouldn't have minded too much if Uruguay kicked Brazil out of it in the semis.

I suspect Sir Alf and the team were all thinking like this because they lost concentration and a feeble shot from Beckenbauer squirmed under Bonetti's diving body. Bell came on for an exhausted Charlton who was obviously being conserved for the semi final on Wednesday. Bell then forced two scrambling saves from Maier but when Libuda was replaced by Grabowski, suddenly the balance of power shifted. Schnellinger lobbed the ball into the England penalty area and the old stager Uwe Seeler, falling backwards as he did so, back headed the ball past Bonetti.

Still England weren't finished. Bell and Ball created a good chance for Hurst but his shot just flashed past the post. Lee, Bell and Ball all went close as the match went into extra time. Our worries now were that England looked exhausted, Germany looked fresher and Grabowski's runs down the wing were ripping into England's tiring defenders. Ramsey brought on Norman Hunter but it was to no avail. Grabowski beat Cooper yet again, centred to the far post where Lohr beat Newton in the air and headed it down for Gerd Müller to beat Labone to it and turn it past Bonetti. 2–3. End of dream.

Sunday 14 June (Cont'd.)

I feel numb. Choked with emotion and numb at the same time. I have never in my whole life felt as badly as this. It's worse than any football result, exam failure, girlfriend problem, you name it. Julie's gone now. It seems ridiculous that I ever thought it meant so much. Who cares? She was just a dumb blonde anyway who didn't care about football. Even my Mum who doesn't give a stuff about football is upset and seems to understand how upset I am. I feel like I'll never eat again, never smile again. Would you believe I've got to answer questions on the Reformation and Charles V tomorrow morning. Life is so unfair.

That was the last entry in my famous World Cup diary. The rest of the exercise book lay blank and yellowing but only slightly. Clearly they made paper from a better class of tree in those days.

I did OK on that European History paper. In fact I did OK on all the A levels. Re-reading the diary it's hard to see quite how it happened but I ended up with a B in History, a B in German and an A in English. I got into Bristol to read English where I met Kate who shortly after my graduation became my wife and now I teach English in a school near Bedford and take charge of the School's Football First Eleven.

It seemed scarcely possible that I would feel as badly about a football match again but I think I did. I think I felt even worse three years later, after that extraordinary 1–1 draw against Poland at Wembley which prevented us from going to the World Cup in Germany in 1974. West Germany stole our place in the semis in 1970 but they also got knocked out in extra time in an amazing 4–3 game against Italy so the Leon defeat was partially avenged almost immediately. Brazil, of course, went on to win the World Cup itself, hammering Italy 4–1 in the final. I dare say Ramsey's side would have put up a better show but I wondered even then, hand on heart, whether any side could have stopped that magnificent Brazilian team.

So that's it then. Ah, perhaps not. You were wondering about Julie, weren't you? Well that defeat by West Germany was followed by the last A level (English History 1815–1914) and an extraordinary sense of lethargy. I was going to vote on the Thursday. I was 18 and three months so I was one of the first eighteen-year-olds to be allowed to vote. It was going to be a kind of declaration of independence after the end of my last exam, a public recognition that I had left school and grown up.

Only I was so depressed by that World Cup defeat that I couldn't be bothered to make the effort. Pretty pathetic I now think, since I take the Sixth Form for General Studies and one of my big speeches when we do the topic of democracy is to bully my kids into voting at every local and general election. It's something I feel really strongly about because, in a way, I suppose I blame myself for letting the Tories win in June 1970.

The day after the election when I saw those ludicrous smiling teeth of Edward Heath on the steps of 10 Downing Street I just thought it had been the worst week in the history of my life. I was going to go down the pub that Friday night and get pissed with the rest of the lads who had finished A levels that day. I was lying on the bed when I heard the doorbell ring and my Mum shouted that there was someone to see me.

I thought it was Jamie and Dan arriving early. Turned out it was Julie, looking, I have to say, unbelievably sexy. I know you'll find this difficult to believe but I really had put her out of my mind the minute that goal from Gerd Müller went in. She looked up at me as I came down the stairs to meet her. Her face broke into that devastating smile – the one that reminded of an 88mm shell exploding. 'Hi,' she said. 'Bummer about the Tories, wasn't it?' I nodded.

'Finished your exams?'

I nodded again. My mother was still standing in the hall.

'I promised your son a present when he'd finished his A levels.'

'Oh,' said Mum, suspecting something fishy but unable to put her finger on it.

'I thought it all depended on England winning the World Cup.'

Now my Mum knew for sure there was something fishy but was no wiser as to its source.

'That was just to make it more interesting,' said Julie. 'But I made you a promise and I always keep my promises.'

And she did. Twice.

A Kickabout in Paradise

Rupert Thomson

It was all a terrible mistake – at least, that was how I felt about it at the beginning. It was June 17th, the first day of the 1994 World Cup, and there I was, sitting in the Metropole Hotel in Alexandria. My room was on the third floor, its French windows opening on to a tiny wrought-iron balcony. From my balcony I could look out over the Eastern Harbour and, if I turned my eyes to the north, I could see the fort that occupied the site once occupied by Pharos, one of the seven wonders of the ancient world. It was a perfect room, a perfect view. All that was missing was a TV. There was a TV in the lounge on the first floor, but it had a piece of paper taped across the screen, which meant, presumably, that it was out of order. I had left London in a quest for peace and quiet, so I could start work on a book, but it had never occurred to me that I wouldn't be able to watch the World Cup at the same time. So far as I could tell, though, nobody in Alexandria seemed remotely interested in the World Cup. Nobody even seemed to know that it was going on.

On my second night in Alexandria I went to a restaurant called Elite. I had chosen the restaurant because it was owned and run by a woman called Madame Christina. When she was a young girl, Madame Christina had known Constantine Cavafy, a Greek poet I had always admired, and I thought it would be interesting to hear what he was like from someone who had actually met him. But when I asked the waiter about Madame Christina, he told me she would not be coming in. She had a fever. To make matters worse, there was no TV in the restaurant – and Brazil were playing their first match of the tournament that night. The opening line of Cavafy's poem 'Of Dimitrios

Sotir' came back to me: *Everything he'd hoped for turned out wrong . . .*

I was just finishing my plate of spaghetti bolognese when a man sat down at my table. He had mischievous brown eyes that sparkled behind his glasses and a bristling moustache. I liked him immediately. He introduced himself as Mohammed, then quickly added that everybody called him Tiger. He was thirty-two and he had lived in Alexandria all his life. He worked in the government's gun factory, which was in the eastern suburbs. He had noticed me the day before, he said, at lunch-time. I had ordered chicken soup. At some point in our conversation I asked him if he was following the football. 'No,' he said, 'I only follow girls.' He wasn't called Tiger for nothing, he said, then he laughed, and there was so much warmth and good humour in his laughter that I found I was laughing too.

Later that night he took my packet of Gold Coast cigarettes and placed his finger over the 't' in 'coast'. Then he looked up at me and smiled.

'I don't get it,' I said.

'Coas,' he said. 'It means pussy.'

And there was that laughter again, infectious, oddly endearing.

The next night I ran into Tiger again, and this time we were joined by three of his friends – Ahmed (known as Little Tiger), Yasser (known as Fox) and Noor, who was just called Noor.

'How was the football?' Tiger asked me.

'I didn't see it,' I said.

'That was my fault,' he said, smiling.

'Only because you're more interesting than football,' I said.

Tiger reached out and shook my hand, which was something he always did when he liked what somebody had said.

And it was true. He was more interesting. For the next two hours he told us gruesome and hilarious stories about his working life in the gun factory. He also told a series of what he called 'Upper Egyptian jokes', which struck me as odd since he was himself from

Upper Egypt. I can only remember one of them now. A man meets a girl and falls in love with her. He goes to his father. Tells his father he wants to marry the girl. No, no, his father says, you can't marry her. She's your sister. The man says, How can that be? When I was young, his father says, I went with many women. Now do you understand? The man goes away. He meets another girl and falls in love with her. He goes to see his father, as before. No, no, you can't marry that girl, his father says. She is also your sister. The man's so frustrated that he goes to his mother and tells her what's been happening. Do anything you like, his mother says. That man is not your father.

It was late when I returned to the Metropole. On my way to bed I was surprised to see a small crowd in the lounge on the first floor. The TV had been mended, and people were watching Greece play Argentina. I arrived in the room just in time to hear the final whistle. I had missed the extraordinary spectacle of Maradona celebrating his first goal of the tournament, a spectacle that only made sense a week later when he failed a urine test. It seemed that my priorities had changed, though. The possibility that I would miss the football if I went to Elite was not enough to stop me going there. It was one of those places that establishes itself as the centre of the universe. I had the feeling that if I sat there for long enough I'd see everything. At the very least I could expect conversation, laughter, jokes. And, every now and then, something dramatic would happen. One night during my second week, for instance, a middle-aged man in a dark-blue sports shirt and pale-blue slacks burst into the restaurant, slammed his wallet and his keys down on the nearest table and began to chase a young Egyptian boy round the restaurant, shouting in strangely guttural English: 'You bloody fucking bastard . . . You prick . . . I'm going to fix you . . . I'm going to cut your balls off . . .' Eventually the waiters persuaded him to leave. When I asked Tiger what the problem was, Tiger shrugged. He told me that the man was the illegitimate son of a French baron. 'He has lived here for many years,' Tiger said. 'He's crazy. Once, he came into Elite and told us that his girlfriend was dead. He was crying for hours. The next week he turned up with her.'

On the one night when I left Elite early enough to watch an entire match, there was a power cut. I walked into the TV lounge five minutes before the kick-off. Italy were playing the Republic of Ireland in New York City. There was Jack Charlton on the touchline in a short-sleeved shirt and a white baseball cap. Looking round the room, I caught the eye of a black man who was smoking a cigar. We smiled at each other. It was because we were in the right place, because we were excited about the game that lay ahead of us. It was anticipation. Then all the lights went out. There we were, about twelve of us, sitting in complete darkness. Nobody reacted, though. Nobody moved. After a while I heard someone sigh. Looking round, all I could see was the tip of the black man's cigar glowing in the darkness. Slowly, as the minutes passed, the atmosphere became more and more surreal. The silence, the darkness. The sound of people breathing. It was like being in a dormitory. How long would we sit there for? Until the game was over? Suddenly the power came back on again. Blinking in the sudden glare, we all grinned at each other self-consciously. The match was only eight minutes old, and the score was still 0-0. Four minutes later Ray Houghton scored the goal that would prove decisive, chesting the ball down, swivelling and beating Pagliuca from twenty yards out, but I couldn't shake off a lingering sense of incompleteness, the same feeling that you have when you arrive at a cinema too late and miss the beginning of the movie.

Halfway through my second week I met up with Tiger and Noor in Elite. Noor sat there with one elbow on the table, his cheek resting against the inside of his forearm. He hardly said a word all evening. When I asked Tiger why Noor was so quiet, Tiger looked at Noor for a moment, grinned and said, 'He has been smoking. That is why.' Finally, just before we left, Noor lifted his head. A smile spread across his face. 'I am very beautiful,' he said. He was trying to tell us that he felt good, of course, but his English had never been up to much, even at the best of times. We all loved the line, though, and kept repeating it over the next few days.

As we parted company just after midnight, Tiger asked me if I would like to go to the beach that weekend.

'We go every Friday,' he said, 'to Abu Qir. We smoke hash and swim in the sea. Do you like to smoke?'

'Yes, I do,' I said.

'You must come with us.'

'I'd love to come,' I said. 'Thank you.'

'Meet us here at two o'clock.'

The World Cup slowly gathered momentum. The USA beat Colombia, largely thanks to an own goal by Escobar, a mistake that would have fatal consequences for him when he returned home. The Republic of Ireland lost 2-1 to Mexico in the 110-degree cauldron of Orlando, and both Jack Charlton and John Aldridge were fined for arguing with a FIFA official. Maradona was suspended from the tournament when he tested positive for drugs.

At five to two on Friday afternoon I was sitting at a table by the window in Elite. Though I was looking forward to the trip to Abu Qir, I was also hoping I'd be back in time to watch Argentina take on Bulgaria; I was curious to see how the South Americans would fare with their best player banished to the touchline. At twenty past two Tiger arrived with Ahmed, Noor and another friend of his called Ghost. Ahmed produced a brown paper bag. Inside the bag was a bottle, which we passed round under the table, swigging from it when the waiter wasn't looking. It was a cough syrup called Pulmolar, which, according to the label on the bottle, contained Dextromethorphan hydrobromide and Chlorpheniramine maleate.

'It makes big head,' Noor explained.

Tiger turned to me with a grin. 'He means that you get high.'

After we had finished the Pulmolar we left the restaurant, but it turned out that Tiger's sister had just given birth to a baby boy, so we had to catch a taxi to Mamsheya Square where we bought a small terracotta vase with a penis on the side. We waited while a man called Bolbol fitted the vase into a basket and surrounded it with cut flowers and sprigs of greenery, then we caught another taxi, this time to Tiger's family home. None of us could go in, though, because we were, as Tiger put it, 'smooth'. Only men with facial hair were allowed into the presence of a new-born baby. It was a tradition. The slightly giddy buzz the cough syrup had given me was starting to wear off, and I was reminded of the time I ate four nutmegs in Athens once because I'd read that they were hallucinogenic; the streets and buildings tilted at odd angles for a while, which was interesting, but the headache that followed was so severe that I felt as if a beam of white magnesium light was being shone directly into my brain. I looked at Ahmed's watch. It was after three o'clock, and we were still in Alexandria. I was beginning to wonder whether we would ever make it to the beach.

At last Tiger reappeared and we walked to a large square near the train station and climbed into a mini-bus. It took another hour to reach Abu Qir, a fishing-town some twenty kilometres east of the city centre. Most of the houses in Abu Qir were only half-finished, their poured concrete still without a coat of paint, and the roads were all unpaved. We met two men on a street-corner not far from Noor's house. One of them wore sunglasses and a T-shirt that said *Blue Water* on the front. The other man had flattened his black hair with some kind of grease or lotion. He was wearing a Hawaiian shirt that reminded me of the Technicolor outfits favoured by Jorge Campos, the Mexican goalkeeper. I noticed that the man in the Hawaiian shirt had the hash concealed between the two middle fingers of his left hand. 'It's so he can throw it away,' Ahmed said, 'if he is stopped by the police.' The men wanted one hundred and twenty Egyptian pounds for the whole lump. Tiger bought half the lump for sixty.

For the next hour and a half we sat in Noor's bedroom with the door closed and the blinds drawn and smoked hash out of a jam-jar. We used the same technique I had used with my brother during the late seventies in Eastbourne, the only difference being that Egyptians inhale through their nose rather than their mouth. Noor's bedroom was extraordinary, with red and green flashing disco lights, a stuffed seagull in a glass case and gilt-framed photographs of Noor in an electric-blue rayon suit at a friend's wedding. We listened to Pink Floyd and a female singer called Mona, then Ahmed put on a cassette of dance music that had been recorded by a plumber in Cairo. Noor served cups of sweet tea and slices of apple on a wooden plate. It was hot in the room, and Tiger and Noor had taken off their shirts. They sat on the bed, running their hands over their bodies with the dreamy complacency of people who have just eaten a fine meal. Once, the door opened and Noor's sister walked in, but when she smelled the air she rolled her eyes and left the room again without having said a word. Ghost talked about angels. Everybody has an angel, he said, but not all angels have people. When I told him I had always thought it was the other way round, he just shrugged and smiled.

At five-thirty, when we had smoked all the hash, Tiger stretched and sighed.

'Now we will go to Paradise,' he said.

I thought for a moment that he was talking figuratively, but he told me that we really were going to Paradise. Paradise was near the gun factory where he worked, he said. Paradise was a kind of holiday resort for workers. We could swim there, if we wanted. We could meet some more of his friends.

We changed into T-shirts and swimming-trunks, then left the house. We walked barefoot through the streets of Abu Qir, stopping every now and then to greet someone. The sun was already low in the sky, colouring the tops of the buildings a deep orange. All around me I could hear the hushed sound of people walking on sand, like the brushes drummers sometimes use in jazz. In ten minutes we reached a pair of tall metal gates, guarded by a man in a dark-green uniform. Tiger spoke to him. He waved us through.

'Now you are in Paradise,' Ahmed said to me with a grin.

It was a model village built on the beach, with thirties-style concrete bungalows and a perfect grid of narrow streets. We went to the beach first, which was crowded, but only Ahmed swam. The rest of us decided that we were too high and that it was too late in the day. Tiger sat beside me and, pointing out to sea, showed me where Nelson had defeated the French fleet at the end of the eighteenth century.

Later, when Ahmed had dried off, we walked back into the village. At the centre of the village was an unpaved square. The concrete bungalows that surrounded it had been painted in pastel colours – frosted pink, lemon yellow, peppermint green. Naked children were playing in the sand; men and women stood about, talking and laughing. I was struck by how open and relaxed Egyptian people were. The hash organised my thoughts into simple, magical sentences. *I'm in Abu Qir*, I thought, *twenty kilometres east of Alexandria. I'm in Paradise.*

I no longer remember how the game began. All I remember is that we were suddenly kicking a football around, eight or nine of us. The ball was made of leather that was as scarred and grey as the skin of an old bull elephant. We split up into teams. The pitch was the square of sand between the houses, the goal-posts were rubbish bins and rusting oil-drums. I was still feeling the effects of the hash and the cough syrup, though, and for the first few minutes I'm not sure I did anything at all.

Then, miraculously, I found that I could run. I was involved in a passing movement that broke down just in front of our opponents' goal. Moments later I won a tackle and sent the ball bobbling across the sand to Noor, who mis-kicked, swore in Arabic, then laughed. I stopped for a moment to get my breath back. I remember noticing a thin moon rising in the soft mauve sky above the rooftops. Bringing my eyes back down to ground level, I saw that Ahmed had the ball. He moved up the left touch-line, then cut inside. Though I had never heard of David Beckham at that point in my life, I took up the kind of position he takes up, floating into the right-hand side of the pitch, midway between the halfway line and the penalty area. Ahmed looked up quickly and saw me standing there, unmarked. He hit a cross towards me, hard and low, about waist-high. I leaned into the ball, meeting it on the volley, and saw it curve smoothly off the outside of my foot, like cream off the back of a teaspoon. As I fell sideways I watched the shot fade past the keeper's outstretched hand and fly into what would have been the top right-hand corner of the net, if there had been a net. Grinning broadly, Tiger reached down and pulled me to my feet.

'You are very beautiful,' he said.

I didn't get back to the Metropole until one in the morning, by which time a lacklustre Argentina had lost 2-0 to the Bulgarians. I had no regrets, though – none at all. I may have missed most of the 1994 World Cup, but at least I can say this: I played barefoot in Paradise.

Contributors

David Baddiel

David Baddiel made comedy history when he became the first British comedian to sell out Wembley Arena. Since then the Writers' Guild award-winner has recorded three series of the hit BBC2 comedy show *Fantasy Football League*, completed a 40-date solo stand-up tour and recorded the Euro '96 single 'Three Lions (Football's Coming Home)'. *Time For Bed*, his début novel, was published by Little, Brown in 1996.

Chaz Brenchley

Chaz Brenchley has made a living as a writer since he was eighteen; this year marks his twenty-first anniversary in the job. He is the author of eight published novels, most recently *Dispossession*, a mystery story about love and death, amnesia and a fallen angel. A prize-winning ex-poet, he has also published three fantasy books for children and close to five hundred short stories in various genres. A spell as Crimewriter-in-Residence at the St Peter's Riverside Sculpture Project in Sunderland led to the collection *Blood Waters*. He lives in Newcastle-upon-Tyne with two cats and a famous teddy-bear.

Tom Bromley

Tom Bromley was born in Salisbury in 1972 and grew up in York. He is currently working part time for Waterstones and taking an MA in Creative Writing at Bath Spa University College, while working on his first novel, 'Goo Goo G'Joob', about the struggles of a struggling rock band. 'The People's Game' is his first published short story. A long-suffering York City fan, he once won a Mars Bar, at the age of eleven, for lobbing Peter Beardsley on a PGL soccer course. He lives in west London.

Jimmy Burns

Jimmy Burns is the author of *The Land That Lost Its Heroes*, about Argentina and the Falklands War, and *Hand of God*, a biography of Diego Maradona. Born in Madrid, he is a past winner of the Somerset Maugham Prize and currently writes for the *Financial Times*.

Ron Butlin

Ron Butlin was born in 1949 in Edinburgh, and brought up in Hightae near Dumfries. A novelist, short story writer and poet, he lives in Edinburgh with his wife and their dog. His books include a short story collection, *The Tilting Room*, and two novels, *The Sound of My Voice* and *Night Visits*. His work has been translated into ten languages and broadcast in Britain, Europe and the US.

Peterjon Cresswell

Peterjon Cresswell was born in 1958 in Mönchengladbach, West Germany, and brought up in the Home Counties. He has worked as leisure and travel editor on the *South East London Mercury*, as leisure editor on *Budapest Week*, and as a writer and consultant on the first *Time Out Budapest Guide* under the editorship of Dave Rimmer, another contributor to this book. He co-wrote *The Rough Guide to European Football*, which topped Sportspages' bestseller list during the autumn of 1997. A mini *World Cup 1998 Guide* followed in March 1998. He divides his time between Budapest's 8th District, Deptford High Street and the Croatian coast, his pockets full of rejection letters for idiosyncratic novels.

Pete Davies

Pete Davies's published works include *The Last Election*, *Dollarville*,

All Played Out, I Lost My Heart to the Belles, This England and *Mad Dogs and English Women*. He has been a contributing editor to *GQ* since 1991. A six-part drama series inspired by his book about the Doncaster Belles was broadcast on BBC TV in May 1998. He lives in Yorkshire with his wife and two children.

David Flusfeder
Born in 1960, David Flusfeder lives in London. He is the author of the novels *Man Kills Woman* and *Like Plastic*.

Maureen Freely
Born in Neptune, New Jersey, and now resident in Bath, Avon, Maureen Freely writes regularly for the *Guardian* and the *Observer*. Her novels include *The Stork Club, Under the Vulcania* and *The Other Rebecca*.

Steve Grant
Steve Grant is the Executive Editor of *Time Out* and writes regularly about arts and entertainment. His plays have been performed in London, Manchester and Edinburgh and include *The Manchester United Show* commissioned by Contact Theatre for the club's centenary. His poetry has been published in Britain and the USA and his short stories anthologised in three collections, including *A Book of Two Halves*. His book *The Essential Neil Young* is published this year. His son, William, is 20 on the day that England play Romania, and 1998 marks the fortieth anniversary of his first World Cup as a fan, and his first visit to Highbury.

Rosie Jackson
Born in Leeds, Rosie Jackson lives in rural Somerset just outside Glastonbury, the setting for her short story. She has published four books of fiction and non-fiction, including *Fantasy: The Literature of Subversion* (1981), *Mothers Who Leave* (1994), *The Eye of the Buddha* (1991) and a biography of Frieda Lawrence

(1994). She has spent the last two years writing a novel based on the Faust myth, which she is now trying to get into print. All she knows about football comes from the men in her life, particularly from her son, a long-time supporter of Aston Villa.

Graham Joyce

The author of six novels – *Dreamside, Dark Sister, House of Lost Dreams, Requiem, The Tooth Fairy* and *The Stormwatcher* (three of which have won the August Derleth Award) – Graham Joyce teaches creative writing at Nottingham Trent University. He was born in Keresley, Coventry and now lives in Leicester with his wife and young daughter. He is a lifelong Coventry City supporter and doesn't mind who knows it.

Christopher Kenworthy

Born in Preston in 1968, Christopher Kenworthy has lived in Garstang, Ludlow, Bath, London and Western Australia. He ran the influential independent press Barrington Books and edited three anthologies of original short fiction, *The Sun Rises Red, Sugar Sleep* and *The Science of Sadness*. His own first collection, *Will You Hold Me?*, is published by The Do-Not Press.

Tim Lawler

Tim Lawler's first short story, 'Villa', appeared in *A Book of Two Halves* (Indigo). 'Gary Sobers' is his second. He has previously had two plays produced in London – *Cheap and Potent* (1990) at The Man in the Moon, and *Plastic Guru* (1991) at The Crown. He has recently completed a novel.

Pete May

Born in Bishop's Stortford in 1959 and a lifelong West Ham fan, Pete May is a journalist living in London. With Andrew Shields and Denis Campbell he co-authored *The Lad Done Bad* (Penguin). His latest book is *Sunday Muddy Sunday* (Virgin), a look at the heart and soul of Sunday league football.

Mark Morris

Leeds United supporter Mark Morris was born in Bolsover in 1963. He has published six novels – *Toady*, *Stitch*, *The Immaculate*, *The Secret of Anatomy*, *Mr Bad Face* and *Longbarrow* – and a short story collection, *Close to the Bone*. He lives in Boston Spa with his wife, the artist Nel Whatmore, and their two children.

Geoff Nicholson

Born in Sheffield and now resident in Brooklyn, Geoff Nicholson is the author of several novels including *The Knot Garden*, *What We Did on Our Holidays*, *Still Life With Volkswagens*, *Hunters and Gatherers*, *Footsucker*, *Bleeding London* (shortlisted for the Whitbread Prize) and, most recently, *Flesh Guitar*.

Ben Richards

Born in 1964, Ben Richards is the author of the novels *Throwing the House Out of the Window* and *Don't Step on the Lines*. His new novel, *The Silver River*, is due in late 1998. He lives in the East End of London and is a supporter of Arsenal Football Club.

Dave Rimmer

The author of *Like Punk Never Happened* (Faber, 1985) and *Once Upon a Time in the East* (4th Estate, 1992), Dave Rimmer was born and raised in Newcastle-upon-Tyne and currently divides his time between London and assorted Central European cities. He supports Newcastle United.

Nick Rogers

Nick Rogers' only previously published work, which appeared in *Random Factor* (Pulp Faction), was an extract from his recently completed novel, *Unputdownable*. Born in Berkeley, Gloucestershire in December 1961, he was brought up in London and Suffolk. At the age of 14 he had trials with Norwich City, Cambridge United and Colchester United. Later he would work as an early morning cleaner at the Institute of Contemporary

Arts. In 1996 he took part in a collaboration with performance artist Bruce Gilchrist at St Thomas' Hospital in which he allowed his brain wave patterns to be monitored as he thought about his unwritten book and later as he slept. He lives in south London.

Colin Shindler
Colin Shindler grew up in a Jewish family in Manchester in the 1950s and '60s. An acclaimed writer/producer, his credits include *Lovejoy*, *A Little Princess* and the feature film *Buster*. His memoir, *Manchester United Ruined My Life*, was published by Headline in May 1998.

DJ Taylor
DJ Taylor is the author of three novels – *Great Eastern Land*, *Real Life*, *English Settlement* – and a collection of short stories, *After Bathing at Baxter's*, in addition to two critical studies. He reviews fiction regularly for a variety of publications. Married, he follows Norwich City and lives in Putney.

Rupert Thomson
Rupert Thomson is the author of five novels – *Dreams of Leaving*, *The Five Gates of Hell*, *Air and Fire*, *The Insult* and *Soft*. Born in Eastbourne in 1955, he has lived in Athens, Sienna, Berlin, New York, Tokyo and Rome, and will be watching the 1998 World Cup in his flat in London.

Conrad Williams
Conrad Williams' short stories have appeared in *Sunk Island Review*, *Panurge*, *A Book of Two Halves*, *Dark Terrors 2*, *Northern Stories 4*, *Sugar Sleep*, *Darklands 2*, *Blue Motel*, *The Ex Files* and elsewhere; his first novel, *Head Injuries*, is published in The Do-Not Press's Frontlines series. He was born in Warrington in 1969 and now lives in north London.

Acknowledgements

'Sportsview' copyright David Flusfeder, 1998

'The Disappointed' copyright DJ Taylor, 1998

'Some of My Best Friends Are German' copyright Dave Rimmer, 1998

'As Seen on Radio' copyright Graham Joyce, 1998

'The Battle of Santiago' copyright Ben Richards, 1998

'Let Your Feelings Slip' copyright Christopher Kenworthy, 1998

'Cheese Crackers' copyright Pete Davies, 1998

'The Killing Fields' copyright Jimmy Burns, 1998

'My Back Pages' copyright Steve Grant, 1998

'Something's Coming Home' copyright Chaz Brenchley, 1998

'Every Four Years We Become a Nation' copyright Ron Butlin, 1998

'Some People Are On the Pitch' copyright Mark Morris, 1998

'England's Shame' copyright Geoff Nicholson, 1998

'1-1-1' copyright Conrad Williams, 1998

'Hysterical Men' copyright Rosie Jackson, 1998

'Love Among the Turnips' copyright Pete May, 1998

'The People's Game' copyright Tom Bromley, 1998

'Where I Go When You're Watching the World Cup' copyright Maureen Freely, 1998

'The Man of Paper' copyright Nick Rogers, 1998

'The Slap of a Frido Five Size' copyright Peterjon Cresswell, 1998

'Gary Sobers' copyright Tim Lawler, 1998

'Maradona: USA '94' copyright David Baddiel, 1998

'Back Home' copyright Colin Shindler, 1998

'A Kickabout in Paradise' copyright Rupert Thomson, 1998